PEACE IS A THREE-EDGED SWORD

PEACE IS A
THREE-EDGED

Lloyd Mallan

PRENTICE-HALL, INC.

SWORD

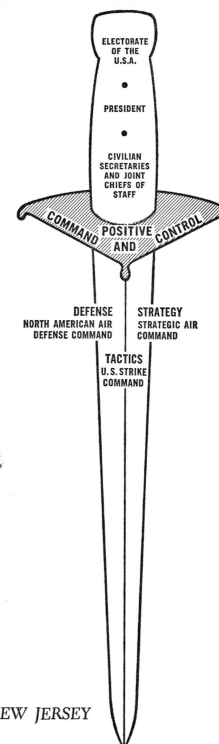

ELECTORATE
OF THE
U.S.A.

•

PRESIDENT

•

CIVILIAN
SECRETARIES
AND JOINT
CHIEFS OF
STAFF

COMMAND POSITIVE AND CONTROL

DEFENSE
NORTH AMERICAN AIR
DEFENSE COMMAND

STRATEGY
STRATEGIC AIR
COMMAND

TACTICS
U.S. STRIKE
COMMAND

ENGLEWOOD CLIFFS, NEW JERSEY

SECOND EDITION APRIL 1964

Some other books by the author

Men, Rockets and Space Rats

Space Satellites

Amateur Astronomy Handbook

Supersonic Project Officer

America's Mightiest Missile

Man Into Space

This book is dedicated to the
Security of the Free World

ACKNOWLEDGMENTS

THE AUTHOR is grateful for the fine cooperation given him by almost 200 persons who helped to make this book possible. These include personnel of the Departments of Defense, Air Force, Army and Navy as well as scientists, engineers and executives of many leading aerospace firms. Naming them all individually here would be impractical in an editorial sense. But at least 87 key persons are identified necessarily as the text of the book unfolds.

To the others, the author can only say: "Thank you for your graciousness in giving so generously of your time!"

Mrs. Rose Tinker Mallan, the author's wife, also deserves emphatic words of thanks for having suffered her way with him through the mountains of material that had to be organized into a concise pattern for this book.

L.M.

FOREWORD

L LOYD MALLAN has taken his open and alert mind, keen pencil and his hungry portable tape-recorder into the major military command centers and the principal research and development agencies of the Department of Defense. He has talked to the Commanders-in-Chief, the research directors and, perhaps of more importance, to the colonels and the captains, the scientists and the technicians who provide the human judgments and skills which give substance and meaning to those organizations.

He has asked the simple questions that are hard to answer. Will this intricate system work in times of great stress? If erroneous human judgment is entered into a command system at a low level, just how is it filtered out before it reaches the top? When one link in the chain is broken, where is the alternate and who energizes it?

He has checked and verified his answers without disclosing information that might be helpful to unfriendly forces. With no inhibition he has asked the questions that the average American would like to ask. He has drawn the conclusions that the average American, including those who like to see the proof behind the assertion, might draw.

I was one of the Commanders-in-Chief who spent several hours with Lloyd Mallan. He spent many days with my staff officers at all levels. He examined my systems, procedures, equipment and facilities up to the full limits of security. I do not agree with every one of his conclusions and I doubt that any of

my contemporaries will. Lloyd Mallan is nobody's patsy. I must
admit, however, that my differences are largely matters of degree
or shade of meaning. And I have no doubt whatsoever that this
book, as a whole, will give the average American an interesting
insight into the military factors which give strength and validity
to our National Policies.

Since so few Americans can visit these many headquarters and
ask these direct and penetrating questions, Lloyd Mallan's *Peace
Is a Three-Edged Sword* provides a satisfying substitute in simple
language.

Laurence S. Kuter
General, USAF (Ret)
Former Commander-in-Chief,
North American Air
Defense Command (NORAD)

CONTENTS

ABOUT the NEED for this BOOK

THREE YEARS of intensive on-the-scene research and roughly 35,000 miles of travel have gone into the writing of the following pages. These were written as a provocative excursion—into realms that are the catchwords of daily existence, realms about which many are strongly opinionated, but which they have never before actually explored. My intention was not only to excite your interest—but to stimulate thinking about the most crucial issues of our day.

The basic purpose of this book is to provide a solid background of information in terms that anyone can understand, with or without a knowledge of science, technology, military operations or foreign policy planning, so that a clear awareness might be derived regarding the complex matrix of national actions and counteractions that superficially are often confusing not only to laymen but to many experts. After the decision was made to write such a book, I discovered that many roads and byways leading to vital background information were forcefully blocked by national security restrictions. Nevertheless, I sincerely believe that I ultimately obtained a true overall picture that will enable you accurately to interpret and evaluate contemporary events upon which the very survival of democracy depends.

Eighty-seven key persons, civilian and military, involved daily with the urgent problems of United States security and defense were interviewed at length, most of them in the presence of a tape-recorder to preserve the nuances of their remarks.

You will be taken behind the scenes to observe the dedication, stamina and intelligence of men working as a closely-knit team to preserve and strengthen the deterrent power of the United States—which is the power of the entire Free World to discourage a potential enemy from starting a nuclear (or any other kind of) holocaust.

You will be shown *factually* why it would be dangerous for you to take any one man's word as absolute in a field that is beclouded with necessary security restrictions. No one "expert," no one newspaperman—no matter how excellent he may be in his own profession—has the right to make pronouncements about the wrongness of other professionals: namely, the military officers and civilians engaged in buildling America's deterrent strength.

You will be shown, not merely told, the meaning of that word "deterrent," how it is developed and why it is necessary for your own survival.

You will also be shown graphically how the numerous airtight checks and counterchecks, human as well as electronic, make it all but impossible for a full-scale nuclear war to be started by accident, madness or hysteria.

You will be further shown how the competetiveness of the free enterprise system and the astuteness plus courage of managerial genius, military as well as civilian, have made it possible for you to sleep without fear.

Finally, you will be given a broad look into the future so that you may obtain an understanding of why military spaceflight on a *routine* daily basis is necessary for the survival of democracy.

The prepublication manuscript of this book, for reasons of both national security and accuracy, had been carefully read by a dozen authoritative persons, civilian and military. One top officer on the Air Staff in the Pentagon made the following comment: "I'm surprised that any publisher would have the courage to print this book—it tells the truth about too many things."

Lloyd Mallan

PEACE
IS A
THREE-EDGED
SWORD

1.

SIX RINGS AWAY
from the GOLD-LINE

"Peace is our profession."

—Motto of the Strategic Air Command

THE MOTTO of the Strategic Air Command is no casual splash of words to delude the public. In fact, it is doubtful that many persons outside of the United States Air Force—including those passionate pamphleteers for world peace—are aware of the existence of this motto. It is not a slogan, which in effect is propaganda. It *is* a motto, a code of existence. It is composed of words that have precise meaning for the men of SAC—from the lowliest airman to the Commander-in-Chief. "Peace" and "Professionalism" are in truth the ideals by which all personnel of SAC live. Those who can't live *daily* by such ideals do not remain long in SAC. For in order to uphold the mission of SAC, a man must not only be experienced, expert and mature psychologically—he must have unusual physical stamina and an almost inhuman dedication to the first word of his motto. The mission of SAC, shorn of all the complex technicalities involved, is to discourage potential enemies of the Free World from even musing on the thought of starting a war, by massive surprise attack or by any other method.

The mission demands three basic accomplishments: One, that SAC's nuclear firepower be second to none. Today, about 85 to 90 per cent of the Free World's nuclear firepower lies within the mixed force of manned jet bombers and unmanned

1

missiles of SAC. Two, that if an enemy should improbably act without reason and initiate a surprise nuclear attack, SAC must be able to absorb the first blow, no matter how massive, and to retaliate with so superior a force that certain defeat for the enemy is swiftly assured. SAC's hidden, hard-site long-range missiles and widely dispersed intercontinental jet bombers on 24-hour ground alert assure this. Three, that SAC itself be a cohesive organization—closely knit on a global scale, synchronized as so many accurate chronometers. Such global synchronization has existed in SAC for at least a decade, if not longer, because of the last word in its motto. It is the world's vastest single organization of professionals in their various fields. The last word makes the first word, "Peace," meaningful.

On this theme I talked at length with General Thomas S. Power, Commander-in-Chief of SAC, at his headquarters, Offutt Air Force Base, near Omaha, Nebraska. General Power is a tall, determined-looking man in his late fifties. He appears at least 10 years younger. His jaw is wide and firm, his eyes blue and alert. A command pilot, he has earned his four stars the hard way, as his decorations testify. He wears the Distinguished Service Medal, the Silver Star, the Legion of Merit with one cluster, the Distinguished Flying Cross, the Bronze Star, the Air Medal with one cluster, the Commendation Ribbon with one cluster and the French *Croix de guerre* with palm. But there are no affectations about him. His manner is informal. He has a reputation for straightforward speech. He maintained that reputation when I talked with him.

"A while back," I began, "Mr. Khrushchev made some pretty threatening statements. He said that the USSR had developed a missile powerful enough to carry a 100-megaton warhead the long way around the world and thus escape our detection systems. From what you know about the USSR's capabilities and your own, how would you answer this?"

General Power seemed almost to smile. "The basic mission of SAC," he started slowly, "is to be prepared to conduct strategic air operations on a global basis, so that in the event of a sudden aggression against this country, a surprise attack, SAC can mount simultaneous nuclear retaliatory attacks *designed* to destroy the war-making capacity of an aggressor to the point where he'd no longer have the will nor the capability to wage war.

"Now the important thing is that the Strategic Air Command *has* the capability to carry out that mission and what's *more* important, is the fact that this is well known to all potential aggressors. We think this has acted as a very potent deterrent to all-out nuclear war.

"Whether you or anybody else agrees with that statement doesn't matter. The important thing is that the record is clean. This world has *not* been engaged in an all-out nuclear war. And that's a *real* good way to keep things, if you can. Because if we ever get into one, there will be no winners—only losers in varying degrees."

"What did you mean by 'destroy the enemy's will'?" I asked.

"Just what I said," he answered.

"But since the Soviets are so treacherous, just how sure can you be that you know where their real targets are? Maybe what you think are targets are merely camouflaged decoy set-ups?"

"We're *sure*," he said quietly.

"You're *sure*? Well, that's very encouraging."

"Besides," he continued, "we have enough force to raise our confidence and assurance factors to an acceptable level; we're not depending on any miracles or luck. It's all based on cold, hard fact."

My next question was inspired by recalling the intense fears of Bertrand Russell and the multitudes of other intelligent, humane persons throughout the world who dreaded the possibility of nuclear warfare. "Wouldn't it be possible," I asked, "for an all-out war to begin by accident?"

"You're asking about the problem of how we deal with a false alarm? I have the authority to launch the bomber alert force upon receipt of warning from NORAD, the North American Air Defense Command. But *only* the President of the United

States or his designated successor can authorize the expenditure of nuclear weapons. Should I ever receive warning that would cause me to launch the bomber alert force, the President and his advisors would have *several hours* of decision time before the bombers must be given final instructions.

"If the warning should prove spurious, the bombers would not receive such instructions and would return *automatically* to their bases after reaching a certain point on their route. If, however, the warning *should* be valid—and missiles impacting in this country would prove this within a few minutes—the SAC alert force would be safely airborne and could be given the order to proceed to their designated targets.

"This Positive Control System permits us to maintain instantaneous combat readiness without the risk of inadvertently triggering a war. Positive Control is indicative not only of the complexity of the problems created by the missile threat but also of the advantages of a manned bomber force in coping with that threat. Unlike our alert aircraft, missiles *cannot* be recalled once they have been launched and, therefore, would have to 'ride out' the initial onslaught of an aggressor."

General Power's last sentence should indicate to even the most indignant lover of peace that the United States is not going to push the panic button and level the world's population by indiscriminately launching squadrons of long-range missiles. If the Soviets "accidentally" launch a few of their ICBMs in our direction, this will not cause us to retaliate on a massive scale. It will only cause SAC to launch the manned bomber force toward preselected Soviet targets, so that the force can be safely in the air if the apparent attack should prove to be real and not accidental. Meanwhile, the President, his advisors and the Joint Chiefs of Staff would have sufficient time to evaluate the situation.

As an example of interest (later to be treated in detail), the mysterious situation that so frightened Lord Russell—when radar reflections from the rising moon were mistaken for Soviet ICBMs—was solved in exactly a minute. SAC bombers did not even have time to become airborne before the alarm was determined to be false.

Another example in the same vein was featured in newspapers throughout the Free World on April 1, 1962. It undoubtedly frightened hordes of well-meaning people into sympathy for that "peace movement" vociferously propagated by the Kremlin to confuse and weaken the Free World's deterrent posture. They did not know the facts, as usual, and the story itself lacked one key fact that transformed the nature of the event. The hard core of the story follows:

The Washington Star said tonight in a copyrighted story that a false signal at the height of the Berlin crisis last Fall indicated the United States might be under attack and hydrogen-bomb-loaded planes even rushed to the runways of Strategic Air Command bases all over the world.

"The bombers did not take off because it was a false alarm," the story added.

Richard Fryklund, author of the story, wrote:

"The four harrowing minutes that the alert lasted revealed a flaw in SAC and Air Defense Command communications. But it also showed that the safety devices that control our retaliatory forces do work, and it proved for the first time that SAC actually has half its bombers on effective 12½ minute alert."

Mr. Fryklund's account continued:

"This is the story, never before told—it was 5 a.m., cold and dark at Omaha, Nebraska. Underground, near the sleeping city, SAC officers were alert, as always, before the huge display boards that would be used to plot the course of a global war.

"Suddenly lights on a signal board indicated that something had gone wrong with BMEWS (Ballistic Missile Early Warning System), the two giant radar stations designed to detect enemy missiles high across the Arctic wastes. . . .

"The officers swiftly informed the boss of SAC, General Thomas S. Power, and also started a check with Air Defense Command headquarters in Colorado Springs, Colorado. . . .

"At the same time, duplicate—even quintuple—electronic circuits made it impossible, in theory, for communications to be cut simultaneously with BMEWS and ADC headquarters. . . .

"For slightly more than 4 minutes war seemed possible. Then, just as suddenly as they were broken, communications between SAC, BMEWS and the Air Defense Command were resumed.

"It was quickly clear that BMEWS was unharmed after all, and no one had hit Colorado Springs. There was to be no war.

"The tension broke at SAC headquarters, but to be completely on the safe side, they let the bombers continue to move to the runways . . . they did not take off. General Power ordered them back to routine alert status."

The *Star* said this story was kept secret by SAC and the Pentagon until today for two reasons:

First, the Pentagon feared that if the public heard about the alarm, people would think mistakenly that this country had gone to the brink of war over an error.

Second, SAC wanted to find the cause of the communications break and correct it before the enemy could find any possible advantage in the incident.

Mr. Fryklund said ". . . the malfunction has been found and corrected."

The impression is clearly given that it took SAC months to find the malfunction and fix it, since up to the time that the story appeared the incident was still security-classified. Actually it took 4 minutes to correct the error. It took only 3 *seconds* to discover the cause. The defect was in a telephone tie-line between SAC Headquarters and NORAD Headquarters. There was no defect whatever between BMEWS, Colorado Springs and Omaha. Nor was there any great tension at SAC Headquarters. The men of SAC, as has already been emphasized, are trained professionals—not romantically impressionable schoolboys. General Power was not trying "to be completely on the safe side" but was merely acting on the basis of logic. Once his combat bomber crews started getting ready to roll, he decided to let them go as a training exercise in taxiing techniques. The more training the SAC crews get, the more proficient they become at their jobs—and those jobs are vital to the security of every American, of everyone in the Free World. General Power attempts to give his men as much training as possible, under conditions as realistic as possible.

These were a few of the things I learned when I visited SAC Headquarters. I also learned about the intense dedication of the men there and throughout the Free World at SAC bases. They work an average of 74 hours a week and are away from home and their families about 135 days each year on alert duty.

Quoting General Power again: "Never before in military history has it been attempted to keep such a high percentage of a large combat force on constant alert in peacetime, let alone to do so month after month and year after year."

At least 50 per cent of the SAC combat crews are on around-the-clock "runway alert" in the United States and overseas. The percentage has climbed quite a bit since SAC first inaugurated the alert system on October 1, 1957. Moreover, the increase has not come out of the taxpayer's salary.

In a special memo to President Kennedy at the close of Fiscal 1962, Defense Secretary Robert McNamara wrote:

> The Air Force has broken new ground in reducing the cost of aircraft maintenance by installing a procedure for the continuous analysis of every part failure on every aircraft. As a result, in Fiscal Year 1962, 4,400 maintenance man-years were released for other assignments, and the equivalent of 45 B-52's and 31 KC-135's (jet tankers for in-flight refueling) was made available for operational service.
>
> These savings made it possible for SAC to increase the B-52 alert posture from a 30 per cent to a 50 per cent alert status without an increase in maintenance resources or operational equipment.

Apart from the runway alert system, SAC continuously trains its combat crews in the procedures of an airborne alert. A full-dress airborne alert system would, of course, be very costly. The essential idea is more ancient than the spear: if your enemy is unaware of your location, he can't find you to hit you. When SAC combat crews are aloft in their bombers, they are highly mobile and dispersed, just as are the Navy's POLARIS-bearing nuclear submarines. An enemy who may be planning a surprise attack must reckon with these imponderables. By simulating an airborne alert on a smaller, less costly, scale, SAC can both train its personnel and keep the enemy guessing.

This proficiency training program assures the survival of a large portion of SAC's retaliatory striking power. In the program, combat crews remain aloft for 24 hours, flying a special pattern that does not infringe upon any potentially hostile nation's territorial rights but which nevertheless encompasses routes that could be used for retaliation in the event of hostilities. When the crews have completed their 24-hour sortie, they wait until replacement crews are aloft in other heavy jet bombers for a similar training mission before they touch down at home base. To insure range and endurance, KC-135 jet tankers service them all. The situation approximates actual combat conditions on a global basis. At the same time, a certain percentage of B-52's is always in the air—around the clock, seven days a week.

POSITIVE CONTROL

Although all SAC combat aircraft and missiles carry nuclear weapons, these are not armed until an attack is commanded by the "GO-Code." This is a closely guarded, secret code available only to the most responsible persons. Even after the code has been ordered and received, it takes a highly coordinated effort by specially skilled crewmen to arm the nuclear weapons. Such weapons are not simple bombs. They are extremely selective units that can be put together in a number of ways to produce a particular amount of yield required to destroy a particular target. No one crewman can accidentally arm these weapons. Nor can he aim and drop them unprovoked if he should break down mentally. Nor can several crewmen go hysterically amok and take their bomber over Russian territory to start a nuclear attack and by this, perhaps, a war. All SAC combat crew members wear side arms—with orders to shoot, if they cannot other-wise subdue, an overwrought recalcitrant fellow crewman.

The same situation prevails at the big operational missile sites. At one TITAN underground control center that I visited, I queried the main combat crew members about safeguards in force to prevent the accidental launching of their devastating intercontinental-range missiles. These men were the Crew Commander, the Guidance Control Officer and the Missile Systems Analyst. All share a 24-hour watch in the control center, after which they are relieved for several days of rest by other combat crews. Such crews are specially trained and chosen for their coolness and maturity of judgement. Yet it takes much more than their finely coordinated skills and mental balance to launch the mighty TITAN.

They described for me—in general terms, since precise details are protected by the highest security classification—the system known as "Missile Positive Control." This system makes it impossible for any single missile crew or crew member to launch their lethal weapons until valid orders are received to do so. The same system applies not only to TITAN but to all Intercontinental Ballistic Missiles—the ATLAS as well as MINUTEMAN.

The order to launch ICBMs can only be authorized by the President of the United States. Once that fateful order is authorized, it is executed by the Commander-in-Chief of the Strategic Air Command, who must first authenticate the authorization. The authentication then simultaneously travels as coded launch orders through multiple communications networks to the missile command posts, where again it must be verified in terms of the code. At the same time, the combat missile control centers are receiving and verifying the code. Even after the code has been verified throughout the vast interlocking system, no combat crew at an ICBM site can launch a missile until electronic devices at the site receive what are known as "launch-enabling signals." These can be transmitted only by the Underground Command Post at SAC Headquarters. In the unlikely event that the key command post should be destroyed by enemy action, the electronic capability to launch or prevent a launch of ICBMs would *automatically* switch to other key command posts. If these should also be destroyed by an enemy, the automatic system would immediately switch the capability to alternate control points. SAC has more than 80 command posts, both ground-based and airborne, throughout the Northern Hemisphere.

This launch-or-no-launch aspect of Missile Positive Control can be likened to a chain of almost numberless invisible electronic keys, each of which fits into a special electronic lock. Unless the right key is mated with its proper lock, the "door" will not open to allow other doors to be opened with succeeding keys. Coupled with the swift opening of electronic doors, all missile-launch personnel must work separately and individually in the most accurate of split-second coordination to fire a single ICBM. The skills and timing required alone preclude the possibility that one or two, or even three, men could launch a missile by accident or with hysterically malicious intent.

Nevertheless, a major motivating theme of those who persistently organize pressure groups to "ban the bomb" is based on the assumption that any minor officer or technician, if he became hysterical or were sufficiently paranoid, could push that fatal button and set the world aflame.

The fact is that an H-bomb warhead is neither a bomb nor a warhead in the conventional sense of those terms. The subject is quite technical and much of it, by nature, must be security-classified. A generalized description, however, can be simply presented. A long- or even medium-range ballistic missile carries not a warhead but a Re-entry Vehicle, known to professionals in the field as an "RV." Inside the RV is a nuclear device, not a bomb, that is shielded by the RV from the high heat generated by friction with the air as the vehicle re-enters the atmosphere from space at a tremendous velocity. Before the RV is launched atop a missile, however, several complicated procedures must be accomplished to arm the nuclear device. Unless the device is armed, it will accomplish no more damage than an empty steel drum of its same size and weight—regardless of how accurately its carrier missile is guided. Finally, the RV is not actually armed until it is ejected from the missile at the top of its trajectory, when the complicated preprogramming to arm it for a specific target goes automatically into effect.

It is rather foolish to assume that either an hysterical or an insane person would be capable of going through the complicated procedures required to program the RV for arming—even if the numerous other counterchecks did not exist.

Yet the American public has become so thoroughly saturated with the nuclear jitters that the Department of Defense itself is jittery about releasing news of minor malfunctions in the defense alarm systems. The fear, naturally, is that the public will misunderstand. In a free society, however, the news is often eventually uncovered by some enterprising reporter and published—out of context. Public misunderstanding is thus heightened. The jitters are intensified rather than diminished.

LITTLE CAUSE FOR NUCLEAR JITTERS

Still, there is little cause for the widespread nuclear neurosis regarding the accidental start of an all-out war. Several of the basic precautions to insure against nuclear accidents have already been described. In February 1962, the U. S. Air Force initiated a world-wide program to investigate human reliability. Other military departments have since launched a similar investigation of their personnel who deal with nuclear weapons. Although no single individual in the Air Force can arm and explode a nuclear device, the program was begun as an additional cross-check in the cause of safety. All personnel who are not high-school graduates have been banned from atomic weapons duty. Such persons are more prone to impulsive acts and boredom, according to the Air Force. Obviously, mentally disturbed persons were weeded out of nuclear service. Even those with the normal tensions of civilized society have been (and are being) carefully scrutinized. A man's family life is investigated periodically. His wife's medical history is studied. His family background, from before his birth to the present, is evaluated. His financial problems are considered. Anything that might now or in the future disturb his emotional maturity is carefully weighed. If there are hints of a mental problem, he is sent to a qualified psychiatrist for further study. This ultrathorough investigation of the human psyche screens out practically all but the most stable of personalities from nuclear weapons assignment.

Control of the use of nuclear weapons is equally watertight. Speaking at the White House Conference On National Economic Issues, May 22, 1962, Secretary of Defense McNamara made this point plain. "The additions to our nuclear power were designed both to strengthen our strategic retaliatory forces," he said, "and also to increase their flexibility by shifting the emphasis to those weapon systems which have the best chances of riding out any kind of nuclear surprise attack. Among the specific measures taken toward this end were: . . . An accelerated program to develop an *effective, protected* command and control system so that at *all times, before, during* and *after* an enemy attack, the constituted authorities, from the President on down, will have *full command* of our military forces." (The italics are mine.)

The command and control system mentioned by Mr. McNamara includes alternate command posts at sea and in the air as well as at individual strategic communications centers. The command post at SAC Headquarters is an excellent illustration of the system. It is buried far underground, beneath the main administration building. High above the building, flying a pattern is the alternate Airborne Command Post. In the unlikely event that the Underground Command Post and its landborne alternates across the nation are bombed out, the Airborne Command Post can instantly take over full direction of the world-wide SAC bomber and missile forces.

Both command posts operate around the clock every day of

every year. Five specially modified KC-135 Jet Stratotankers comprise the Airborne Command Post, which has communications equipment duplicating the equipment underground. Regardless of the weather, one KC-135 is always airborne—and the winter weather of Nebraska can be rugged. One SAC officer told me that he has known these KC-135s to take off and land with ice on the runway, in conditions of zero visibility. The big jets rotate in 8-hour shifts. The one that is aloft does not descend for a landing until its replacement has taken over control. Each aircraft is headed by a general officer—in fact, General Power has done his stint aloft—and a staff that includes a Control Officer, Communications Duty Officer, an Airman Controller and two radio operators. The general's title is Airborne Emergency Actions Officer.

As soon as the command post is airborne it establishes ultra-high-frequency and single-side-band communications with the main command post underground, the United States Air Force Command Post and the Joint War Room, both in Washington, D.C., more than a thousand miles away.

Before writing this chapter, I requested permission to visit the Underground Command Post at SAC Headquarters. It was granted, with one condition. I was not permitted to enter the targeting room. After several hours of asking questions in that vast subterranean chamber of concrete, steel and electronics, I was convinced of two things. Nobody is going to start a nuclear holocaust by accident, even if the United States is attacked by accident. But if the United States or any of its allies is attacked intentionally, the aggressor will have committed suicide as surely as if he had stood facing the mouth of a cannon and given the order to fire.

At the entrance to the Underground Command Post are two SAC Control Center Elite Guards, wearing side arms and dark blue berets. Unsmiling but courteous, they appeared to take with more than average seriousness their jobs of maintaining maximum security. Other Elite Guards appeared occasionally as my SAC escort and I walked downward through austere concrete corridors that sloped and turned unexpectedly. The walls and ceiling were a drab gray. Stacked along the sides of the walls were cases of C-rations, stored there in the event of an emergency that would cause the command post to be sealed off from the world. Every several hundred yards we came to a thick steel blast-door that could, if necessary, hermetically seal that portion of the tunnel. Finally, we arrived at our first stop, the underground radio station.

On one wall, beside a 24-hour clock, was a chart of the Northern Hemisphere. From the North Pole downward, it displayed the accurate relationships between all of North America, the USSR and China. Except for these last two nations and India, the map was dotted profusely with small amber lights. These lights marked the positions of SAC installations in Saudi Arabia, Turkey, Libya, Morocco, England, France, Spain, the Azores, Greenland, Bermuda, Puerto Rico, Hawaii, Guam, Japan, Okinawa and various portions of the North American continent, including Labrador, Newfoundland, Canada, Alaska and the United States proper.

The lights blinked on and off as the radio operator carried on a series of quick voice conversations in coded language. When he paused temporarily and we were introduced, I asked him what the legend above the chart meant. It read: "SAC Commanders SSB Net." He explained that the SSB stands for Single Side Band and that the Commanders Net is SAC's global communications radio network. Single-side-band radio transmission and reception is much more reliable and interference-free than the more conventional short-wave radio communications systems. To demonstrate the system for me, the operator picked up the microphone and called Spain, England, Libya, Greenland and Hawaii in rapid sequence. Each acknowledged him instantly. Two of the stations whose code names he had called were heavy bombers flying high over Hawaii and Labrador.

I mentioned that I knew of the big antenna "farm" at Elkhorn, Nebraska, from which his signals are sent around the world. "But suppose an enemy destroyed those antennae—they're all above ground—how would you communicate with the SAC commanders then?" I asked him.

He shrugged. "We have auxiliary antennae upstairs, on the roof of the headquarters building."

I thought I would stump him. "All right, suppose the Headquarters Building is demolished by a nuclear blast from an enemy missile?"

He was not stumped. "We have an emergency antenna system down here," he explained. "It's like a long steel spike. If it has to be activated, it will automatically bore its way straight up through all the rubble, until it is in the clear."

SAC thinks of everything. I thanked him, and we proceeded farther into the depths of the earth, until we reached the Control Room. It was huge and impressive. About 140 feet long and nearly 40 feet wide, the ceiling was certainly more than 20 feet high. One entire lengthwise wall of the room, except for a small quarter-area, was covered with a giant projection screen that stretched almost from the floor to the ceiling. Facing the screen was a long row of desks at which at least a dozen senior master sergeants sat, busily writing notes as they talked on telephones. Other high-ranking noncommissioned officers were sporadically interrupting them to discuss some point of interest on a newly received sheet of operational data. Most of these data came from a battery of high-speed electronic IBM digital computers located in another room and were received on an automatic printer. Occasionally, the senior master sergeants would mark the data sheet in order to emphasize a particular block of information. The sheets were then quickly copied on transparent film in a dry-process developing machine. Two of these machines were in constant use on a table behind the desks. Also to the rear of the desks was a 10-foot high platform that extended the length of the room, in front of an inward slanting glass window. Atop the platform, spaced at equal intervals, were six large optical projectors. Sergeant-specialists were clambering onto the platform to insert film in the projectors or standing on ladders to adjust their focus onto the screen. Behind the long glass window was another room with another extensive row of desks at which sat commissioned officers, equally busy with telephones and consultations. They had a clear view of the screen through the platform supports. Above the platform, also in the rear wall, was a second huge plate-glass window—this one slanted outwardly to avoid glare and reflections from the many desk lamps below. Behind this window sat the battle staff of SAC's Commander-in-Chief. In time of war, General Power himself or his counterpart would sit there. Now, his appointed deputies watch the screen and continually advise him of the current information. Very often, he sits in also.

If a global war should occur, the electronic computers would record the progress of SAC's strike force on a world-wide basis, providing the Commander-in-Chief with immediate moment-by-moment knowledge as a vital background for him to make swift and accurate decisions. Within 30 seconds, such vital operational data can be taken from the original printed source and projected on the screen before the entire battle staff.

CLOCKS OF SPECIAL INTEREST

Although the Control Room ceiling is hung with fixtures containing banks of more than a thousand fluorescent lighting tubes, they are rarely turned on except when the men change shifts or when technical repairs are required. Flashed on the screen were a variety of maps and charts. In the nearly dark room they appeared dramatically significant.

Among the subjects projected were "Missile Activity" (research and/or training launches at Cape Canaveral on the east coast of Florida, at Vandenberg Air Force Base, adjacent to the Pacific Ocean in California, and at the Air Proving Ground Center at Eglin Air Force Base on the Gulf coast of Florida), "Materiel Status," "Weather Status," "Air Refuel Areas" and "Reflex Action Bomber."

To me, the most interesting part of the screen side of the room was a group of eleven clocks hanging over the screen, from the ceiling at almost dead-center. Eight of these clocks hung in front of maps. All were in square steel cases of different colors —red, yellow, gray, blue and so forth—and displayed the time numerically in terms of the 24-hour scale. The clocks had place-name signs attached to them. I asked my escort to explain the purpose of the signs. His answer was rather magnificently understated. "These clocks indicate time in areas of the world which are of interest to SAC." One of the clocks was tagged "Moscow"; beside it was another marked "Omsk."

Code names marked on the projected maps were typically, colorfully, wittily American: "Bridesmaid," "Elsewhere," "Able-body," "War-Horse" and "Short Punt"—to name a few. Progress of these and all other operations on charts as well as maps was indicated continually and dynamically: the film in the projectors could be marked with numbers, flight-path or missile-trajectory track lines and coded symbols simply by using colored grease pencils or crayons. The superimposed markings showed up vividly on the screen.

After we left the huge Control Center room, my escort guided me around several corners into the back rooms to meet Colonel Merle M. Jones, the senior controller on duty at the time.

Colonel Jones, like everybody who was working in his immediate vicinity, wore a .38-calibre side arm. He was an affable, serious man who made a considerable effort to brief me thoroughly on the control and command system in his charge at the moment. Beside his control console were three colored telephones. One was red, one was gold and one was blue. The blue phone was used for normal communications. The red phone represented the famed "hot-line" that is the prime alerting system at SAC Headquarters. By picking up this phone, Colonel Jones could instantaneously talk with every SAC Command Post throughout the world. All he had to do first was press the red Alert Button on his compact telephone switchboard. He demonstrated the system for me on a nonalert basis. The switchboard also contained six long rows of transparent buttons, each representing a separate command post. When one of these but-

tons lit up, Colonel Jones knew he was being called by a particular command post. Here is how he simulated an alert for me:

He pressed the red Alert Button as he picked up the "hot-
line" phone and said, "This is a test. I'm checking reliability.
Respond immediately if you read me clearly." Before he had the
phone back in its cradle, all the buttons were lit on his switchboard.

He pressed several of the buttons and talked with places as
diverse as Guam and Puerto Rico before he called off the "test."

Colonel Jones also explained why the communications system is practically foolproof. It makes use not only of land-wire
and transoceanic cables, but also of single-side-band backup and
alternate cables and telephone lines as well as a radio- and wire-
teletype network. Electronic pulses travel throughout the whole
system every 3 seconds at the speed of light. This would be
a velocity of almost 186,000 miles per *second*. The pulses do not
interfere with messages or conversations: they are electronically set to ride over these. If at any time there is a malfunction
anywhere in the communications control system, the pulses will
locate and report it within a maximum period of 3 seconds. The
defective part of the system would automatically be by-passed
by immediate transfer to an alternate circuit.

A graphic instance of how effectively the control system works
was recalled by Colonel Jones. "Sometime ago," he said, "a Russian fishing trawler cut the transatlantic cable we were using.
We were out of communications on that line for less than 3
seconds. When the pulses were stopped at the break, the system
automatically switched over to another cable."

More pertinently, SAC's control over its nuclear missiles and
bombers can never be delayed for more than 3 seconds. So much
for Lord Russell's intense concern over the possibility that "mechanical defects" will one day be the cause of a devastating
nuclear war.

There remains, of course, the unpredictable enemy. Suppose,
in a moment of insanity, he decides to attack with nuclear weapons? How will the world survive if we respond with nuclear

retaliation? At this point, the gold telephone pre-empts the stage to answer these urgent questions.

If Colonel Jones should ever have to pick up the gold phone, he would instantly have a direct line to the President of the United States, the Joint Chiefs of Staff, the Commander-in-Chief of NORAD and all other major command headquarters concerned. The gold phone would only be used if an attack is, in fact, progressing against North America or our allied nations. Its one purpose is to assure that the situation is kept under strict control, that nobody goes hog-wild on a spree of destruction, that the correct decisions are made to strike back *selectively* and *decisively*.

ULTIMATE WEAPONS

The triple purpose of America's military deterrent power has already been stated. It is to discourage a surprise attack by an enemy, to be able to withstand that initial attack if it does occur and to effectively, as soon as possible, paralyze the enemy's ability to wage further warfare. The counterattack would be selective in that the United States would not immediately launch giant missiles toward the enemy's homeland. These missiles, hidden underground and protected, are insurance that an enemy will not start anything without pausing to think first of their presence. They are the ultimate weapons, to be used only as a last resort. Backing them up are the POLARIS missiles, stored in submarines roving at will under the seas surrounding the enemy. Although the final Presidential decision on the counterattack approach must depend upon the exact nature of the attack, the bomber squadrons of SAC would probably be ordered into battle first. And SAC air bases around the world, as well as within the United States, are located in a pattern that makes it possible swiftly to hit the enemy from all points of the compass. He's boxed in—and he knows it.

SAC air bases—as well as the SAC ballistic missile bases—are widely dispersed in such a manner that it would be extremely difficult, if not impossible, for an enemy to knock them out all at once in a massive surprise attack. Deactivating one or two would be his *best* hope. Even then, a major percentage of the SAC bombers would have sufficient warning to be airborne and on its way before the base was struck. An added risk to the enemy has already been mentioned: an effective number of the big bombers is *always* in the air on training missions.

Many of the bombers carry what SAC calls "penetration aids." As the phrase implies, these are electronic devices to confuse an enemy's defense-detection systems and divert them from SAC weapons that can be launched toward his vital targets from great distances. The latter are known as Air Launched Cruise Missiles (ALCM). The ALCM is already operational on the B-52G bomber. Popularly designated as the "HOUND DOG," it can guide itself 500 miles to destroy a target with a nuclear blast, after it is released by the bomber crew. Since it is propelled by a ramjet engine, it can also supply auxiliary power to its carrier, the B-52, thus permitting the bomber to carry an extra heavy load of other weapons. Two HOUND DOGs, mounted beneath the wings and aligned with the bomber's standard turbo-jet engines, transform the B-52 temporarily from an eight-jet to a ten-jet airplane. The HOUND DOG engines can be started without releasing the missiles, to provide additional power at take-off. This would also permit take-off from emergency runways normally too short for the big bomber.

Among the devices to confuse an enemy's radar is "QUAIL." This is a small decoy that, once launched from a bomber, shows up on the radar screens as the blip of a B-52. By launching a number of such decoys in one direction, the enemy's antiaircraft firepower can be diverted while the real B-52's proceed unhindered in another direction.

Other penetration aids that are in the works are security-classified.

It can be seen that the manned bomber is hardly obsolete, as so often we have been led to believe. The big ballistic missiles —both intercontinental- and intermediate-range—are indispensable, however. They stalemate the enemy in other vital regions of warfare and have additionally made possible the scientific exploration of space. But they do not replace—they complement—the manned bomber.

COUNTERSTRIKE-IN-DEPTH

SAC has developed a manned-bomber counterattack technique that may be aptly described as "counterstrike-in-depth." The concept arose from need to convince an enemy that it would be impossible for him to be victorious if he attacked. Its aim is to give him an excellent reason *not* to attack. It is the Blue-Amber-Red-Area strike approach. With this method, SAC bombers can *continuously* pound away at the enemy's strategic targets until his industrial and war-making capabilities are thoroughly devastated. They can do this with selected nuclear weapons that contaminate only the local area of the target.

The Blue Area is outside enemy territory. It is a rendezvous area across a wide front, where KC-135 Stratotankers wait for the bombers at selected positions.

The Amber Area is within enemy territory, but not deeply.

The Red Area is deep within the enemy's homeland.

Each fully fueled bomber flies directly to the Red Area and destroys its assigned targets. On the return trip it strikes at targets in the Amber Area before being forced, with fuel becoming depleted, to leave enemy territory for the Blue Area, where it meets a jet tanker and is fully refueled. The bomber wings again toward another Red Area, and the whole process is repeated. The big bombers finally return to their home base, or to an auxiliary base, to replenish their cargo of weapons and allow the crews to rest before starting off again. The result is a ceaseless bombardment from endless waves of B-52's on airborne missions of 24 hours or longer, with each crew spelling out another crew, no matter how widely scattered are their home air bases. Types and locations of targets, of course, are ever-changing because an enemy tries to survive by shifting his concentrations of troops and equipment, but SAC crews are prepared in advance to meet and counter these changes. As Captain Jack Olsen, a

SAC man for many years, told me, "Even the crews on practice alerts know the target lists as well or better than they know the furniture in their own living rooms." These target lists can vary from week to week, day to day. The precise coordination of the extremely diverse elements involved in the Blue-Amber-Red-Area concept is made possible by the global control system at the command post beneath SAC Headquarters.

Such tight control on a world-wide scale is possible not only because of the incredible communications system but also because of the previously mentioned IBM electronic computers. These "brains" can store, recall and analyze 40,000 coded words a minute. They "memorize" information on the status of SAC aircraft, missiles, crews, bases, war plans and supplies. They also aid experts in the Intelligence Trajectory Center mathematically to establish target-trajectory and space data for SAC's Intercontinental Ballistic Missiles. This information is fed electronically into the long-range missile guidance systems that steer the nuclear Re-entry Vehicles to a precise position in space, from where they can accurately fall on their targets.

The same bank of electronic brains during actual warfare would automatically and continuously keep the strike information up to the moment for the Commander-in-Chief of SAC and his Joint Strategic Target Planning Staff. Since SAC's Emergency War Plan is fluid and continually must be changed to meet changing enemy situations, the high-speed computers are an invaluable daily tool of the JSTPS.

The JSTPS is an outstanding example of interservice *cooperation*. General Power is the Director. His Deputy Director is Vice Admiral Roy L. Johnson, former Assistant Chief of Naval Operations for Plans and Policies. His Chief of the Liaison Group with the Joint Chiefs of Staff is the Army's Brigadier General William R. Peers. The JSTPS has more than one hundred permanently assigned personnel from the Army, Navy, Marine Corps and Air Force. There is no rivalry among these men. They are all highly skilled intelligence or operations specialists. Their job is to analyze strategic target information and develop the target lists from which they devise an integrated strategic war plan on the basis of weapon systems assigned to each branch of all the military departments. In a phrase, they synchronize the most efficient use of all the strategic systems—bombers, fighters, land-based missiles and missile-armed Naval vessels and submarines—throughout the world.

Professional efficiency and businesslike management are keynotes of SAC.

They are also keynotes of the North American Air Defense Command. The Combat Operations Center of NORAD as well as its Commander-in-Chief are continuously linked with the Strategic Air Command by around-the-clock communications every day of the year. Offense and defense are two sides of the same sword.

NORAD's Situation Display System is directly tied in with SAC's Underground Command Post. The SDS is an electronic system that visually shows incoming aircraft or missiles on an Iconorama screen. So far, fortunately, no missiles have appeared on the screen—although a number of unidentified aircraft have appeared. These appear as white luminous lines moving across a map of the North American continent and surrounding ocean areas. The aircraft were, of course, quickly identified as friendly off-course vehicles. But in the case of a surprise attack against the United States, NORAD and SAC would know immediately the direction, progress and magnitude of the attack. Reaction would be swift.

Such a situation will certainly never occur—if the enemy is rational. Thus far we can depend on his rationality. The consequences to him and to his nation if he attempts to attack the Free World are too obvious and too irrevocable.

The red and gold telephones are on the desks of men who know their business well, who can make intelligent decisions. I learned that none of them is ever permitted to be more than six rings away from the red- or gold-lines.

I asked General Power: "Is it true that you can never be more than six rings away from a telephone, even when you're on a golf course?"

He nodded. "Either myself or my deputy, General McConnell—one or the other of us must always be within six rings of the telephone. That's maximum."

It is also maximum for the President of the United States, the Joint Chiefs of Staff and the Commander-in-Chief of NORAD—or their appointed deputies.

2.

HOW VULNERABLE
is the FREE WORLD?

"Anyone who today takes a pessimistic view of our air
defense capability is plainly not up to date on the facts
of the case."

—*General Robert M. Lee, USAF,
Air Deputy to the Supreme Allied Commander,
Europe; formerly Commander,
U. S. Air Defense Command*

APPROXIMATELY 500 miles to the southwest of SAC
Headquarters in Nebraska, a great cavern has been
hollowed out of the solid granite of Cheyenne Mountain in the Colorado Rockies. Not far from here lie the 500
acres of strangely beautiful rock formations suggestively named
"Garden of the Gods." Below, at the 6,000-foot level, within the
limits of the plateau-city of Colorado Springs, is Ent Air Force
Base, headquarters of the North American Air Defense Command. Lording it over the total scene is the snow-tipped grandeur
of Pikes Peak. If the West Coast were taken to be the head
and shoulders of the United States, then Colorado Springs
would be located in the approximate position of its heart. This
is appropriate, for NORAD *is* the heart in defense of the North
American homeland. Viewed from the air, the scene is peacefully picturesque—a quiet little resort city of quaintly mixed
buildings, old and new, surrounded by peaks, crags and foothills strongly etched against the severe blue of the sky. Among

25

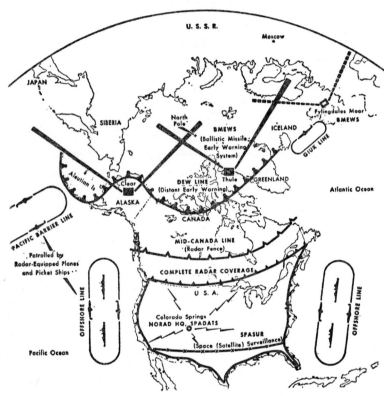

Continent-Guarding Radar Webs

the buildings are three five-story concrete rectangular blocks enclosed with barbed wire. In front of these, the flag of the United States and the ensign of Canada fly on tall poles against the background of Pikes Peak. The three austere buildings are a clean, bright ochre in the clear mountain air—but they are also defenseless. Enemy missiles, soaring across the top of the world with sufficient accuracy, could conceivably knock them out. For this reason a huge cavern was carved inside of a granite mountain, 2,000 feet below its summit.

The three buildings house the Combat Operations Center (COC) of NORAD. They are to the aerospace defense of North America what the SAC Underground Command Post is to global strategic offense. The two control centers are interdependent in terms of discouraging an enemy surprise attack against *any* Free World nation allied with the United States. For in order successfully to attack and vanquish our allies, an enemy must first neutralize the retaliatory power of the United States. He must destroy our SAC forces and our industrial war-making capability on all fronts. This is unlikely enough to be called impossible at the present time. The NORAD alarm system would have SAC bombers in the air and SAC missiles at the ready before an enemy could reach our shores with long-range missiles or manned bombers. In the latter case, the enemy would not stand even a gambler's chance of getting through our defenses with more than an inadequate few of his destructive weapons—if he could achieve that much. The combat arms of NORAD are too well organized and lethal to permit this. They include the Air Defense Command of the Air Force, also headquartered at Colorado Springs, with a variety of supersonic interceptors and the deadly longer range type of ground-to-air missile, called BOMARC; the NIKE-HERCULES aerospace defense missile batteries of the Army; the early-warning barriers, anti-submarine and offshore picket patrols of the Navy; and the Air Defense Command of the Royal Canadian Air Force, with its own variety of defense weapon systems plus a few types of systems provided by the United States.

The stakes are much too high, however, for NORAD to take chances with the future. Hence, work has been continuing feverishly to establish the Combat Operations Center within the secure granite walls of the Cheyenne Mountain cavern.

When it is completed in the Spring of 1965, the new COC will be practically invulnerable. A precisely direct hit by a multi-megaton thermonuclear bomb or ICBM Re-entry Vehicle *might* destroy this COC—or it might only melt away a portion of the mountaintop. The main tunnel, located in the side of the almost 9,500-foot-high mountain at an altitude of about 7,000 feet, is a mile in length from portal to portal. The granite-encased cavern itself will be subdivided into seven chambers for the electronic and communications control equipment. There will also be power stations, fresh-water reservoirs and food storage compartments. An organization of 700 persons will be able to live and work in the 200,000 square feet of floor space available. The new, almost impregnable Combat Operations Center will duplicate exactly the present group of three five-story concrete buildings, with all personnel and equipment.

WILL ABSORB NUCLEAR SHOCKS

The many-chambered structure of this future COC will be enclosed in a steel housing mounted on gigantic coiled springs within the granite cavern. Designed to absorb the shock waves produced by nuclear blasts, the springs thus would protect personnel from injury and equipment from damage in the event of a direct hit on or near miss of the mountain—two quite unlikely events. Blasting out the tunnels and cavern as well as the structural construction work has been the responsibility of the U. S. Army Corps of Engineers, Omaha District. Colonel H. G. Woodbury, engineer for the District, claims that the springs are "the largest we know of ever used to support a structure." He adds that the steel wire from which the springs are drawn is 3 inches in diameter, the largest ever made. The coils themselves will be about 3½ feet high and 2 feet in diameter. In the process of hollowing out Cheyenne Mountain, 450,000 cubic yards of granite had to be carted away. Simple numbers barely give an image of the engineering magnitudes involved in this job, but they should at least suggest the formidable persistence and skills of men devoted to the defense of democracy.

The new Combat Operations Center will cost the American taxpayer more than 88 million dollars before it is completed in early 1965. Is it worth that kind of money? A glance into the functions of the present vulnerable COC should supply an answer.

A situation analogous to that of the COC would be the performance of a powerful magnifying lens. Placed in the midst of a scattered array of broad-beamed searchlights, the lens could focus the diverse light rays to a finely sharp point. The COC accomplishes a similar effect with the beams of radar and other radio detection devices spread from the waters of the Atlantic to those of the Pacific and across the North American land masses from the Mexican Border to beyond the North Pole. NORAD's attack-detection network is designed to provide ample warning of the approach of unidentified aircraft, missiles or space vehicles, such as satellites. Its radar coverage not only completely encircles the United States and extends through hundreds of miles over the surrounding seas, but also stretches across Canada, Greenland, Alaska and throughout the chain of Aleutian Islands. At all hours of the day and night, electronic information from this far-flung network is continuously and instantaneously fed into the big computers at the COC in Colorado Springs, where it is translated as the movement of objects through the air and space and projected visually onto big motion-picture-type screens.

Ceaselessly, NORAD observers watch these screens to follow the positions of airborne (or spaceborne) objects thousands of miles away from the Center. The electronic computers automatically compare the positions displayed with the positions of known friendly vehicles. A daily record is kept of all aircraft movements, both military and commercial. If the position on display does not match the position of a known vehicle, an alarm is given to the Air Defense Command of the Air Force. The ADC swiftly sends its supersonic fighter-interceptor aircraft aloft to investigate and identify the "unknown." Thus far, of course, the unknowns—called "bogeys" by the fighter pilots—have been friendly aircraft that have strayed off course.

There have also been "missile attacks" that almost immediately were determined to be false. An example will be described shortly.

The complex, incredibly imaginative and yet reliable attack-detection systems of NORAD were achieved only because of military-industrial teamwork. The same teamwork holds true in the development of the weapon systems used for air defense as well as for the unprecedented strategic and tactical weapon systems that make America's deterrent strength so credible to any potential enemy.

Extending farthest north are the radar beams of the Ballistic Missile Early Warning System, mentioned in the previous chapter. Prime contractor for BMEWS was the Radio Corporation of America. Three prominent subcontractors were General Electric Company, Sylvania Electric Products and Goodyear Aircraft Corporation. These companies were given an "impossible" task. They had to produce a system of radars that would fan out, overlapping their beams, across the top of the world for 3,000 miles to survey huge sky areas of the USSR, including Siberia, Asia and Europe. No radar had ever before been effective at such distances. The BMEWS radars—located at Clear, Alaska; Thule, Greenland, and Flyingdales Moor, England—effectively cover every logical route that a long-range ballistic missile would take enroute to the United States or the United Kingdom from launching points in the Soviet Union.

Western Electric Company had the prime contract for the design and installation of a subsidiary, but equally important, system that would have startled the most advanced dreams of Alexander Graham Bell. It is the comprehensive communications system, employing multiple channels that complement each other to assure absolute reliability in the transfer of detection and tracking information from the BMEWS radars to NORAD's Combat Operations Center, and from there to the

Command Post at SAC Headquarters as well as to the Air Force Command Post and the Joint War Room in the Pentagon. The British Royal Air Force is also a vital link in the network, which goes by the official title of BMEWS Rearward Communication System.

SAFETY IS BUILT IN

To assure against the introduction of errors (and thus perhaps false alarms) into the system, there is a built-in self-correcting feature. Every thousand miles along the route, the data being transmitted from the BMEWS sites are automatically checked for errors. The same automatic electronic check is made again at the receiving stations. If there is the slightest thing wrong with the coded messages at any checkpoint, the sending station at a particular BMEWS site is ordered to retransmit the message and does so until a correct message is received. The whole process takes mere fractions of a second. Supplementing the coded data transmissions are additional circuits that provide voice and teletype communications. The BMEWS Rearward Communication System is probably the longest network ever built for communications. Its routes encompass more than 45,000 miles, a distance equivalent to twice that around the equatorial bulge of the Earth.

Yet if this network appears to be an heroic achievement of science and technology, the giant radar-detection antennae at the BMEWS sites in Greenland and Alaska are even more incredible. Each of the seven antennae is larger than an upturned football field, or 400 feet long by 165 feet high. The backstay girders that support them, spaced at about 25-foot intervals, are at least 70 feet long. Each antenna weighs almost 2 million pounds.

Behind the conception, as well as the success, of the Ballistic Missile Early Warning System was the Air Force Systems Command. The AFSC's major mission is to uncover advanced scientific and technological concepts through research and develop these into operational systems that can be turned over to the other major Air Force commands to bulwark the deterrent power of the Free World. A credo of AFSC is to be always *at least* 5 years ahead of the enemy, with a 10-year lead as an actual goal. The Electronic Systems Division of AFSC, through its BMEWS Program Office, was chief manager in the development of an ICBM-attack-detection system that broke all precedent in electronic science and engineering.

South of the BMEWS radar beams, snaking its way through the Aleutians, the northernmost borders of Alaska and Canada and across Greenland to the edge of Iceland, is the Distant Early Warning Line, more popularly known as the DEW Line. This is a long chain of shorter range radars that continuously overlap to assure an advance warning of several hours in the event of a manned-bomber attack over the polar regions from Russia.

To the east of the DEW Line is the GIUK Line, which gets its name from the initials of Greenland-Iceland-United Kingdom. It is a mobile type of radar surveillance, an around-the-clock patrol of radar-equipped airplanes and picket ships.

To the west of the DEW Line is the Pacific Barrier Line, another mobile surveillance system, identical with the GIUK Line, except for the area patrolled.

Both of these seaward extensions to the DEW Line are provided by aircraft and ships of the U. S. Navy.

Six hundred miles due south of the DEW Line is the Mid-Canada Line, a microwave radio "fence" that makes use of a special technique called the "doppler shift" to determine accurately the direction and speed of aircraft passing through its cones of microwave radio-energy. From the Canadian Atlantic to the Canadian Pacific, it forms a continuous net in the sky, enmeshing all airborne objects flying at low altitudes. If a fleet of Russian bombers, seeking to escape detection as they invaded over the polar regions, were to come in low under the DEW Line (designed specifically for detection at higher altitudes and thus having only a moderate low-altitude capability), those bombers would most certainly be detected by the Mid-Canada Line early enough for defense against them. The Mid-Canada

Line was built and is manned by the Royal Canadian Air Force, an integral part of the NORAD organization.

A few hundred miles farther south at the United States-Canadian border, an adjoining line of radars, formerly called the "Pinetree Line," is also manned by the RCAF. It, too, stretches continuously from the Atlantic to the Pacific Oceans and is on radar-alert around the clock for unknown airborne interlopers.

Other continuous radar systems fence in the continental United States from the tip of Maine to the tip of Florida, around the curve of the Gulf of Mexico, up the United States-Mexican border and from San Diego northward along the edge of California to the uppermost part of the state of Washington. Two Offshore Lines of mobile radar-aircraft and picket ships flank the United States from several hundreds of miles out in the Atlantic and Pacific Oceans. These are supported by USAF aircraft and, again, U. S. Navy ships. On the Atlantic side, also, the big Texas Tower radars have been replaced by an automatic airborne system that can identify hostile aircraft in 1½ seconds.

Since the direction of a surprise bomber attack would be at the enemy's choice, NORAD has all the conceivable approaches under the strictest radar watchfulness. As of this writing, it is doubtful if a needle could get through the total radar network without detection.

In the late Spring of 1962, a low slow-flying light airplane escaping from Cuba *did* get through to Florida without detection. This could not happen again, however. Long before the incident, NORAD had anticipated such a possibility. The design and construction of Gap-Filler Radars had been in progress. They were installed one month after the anti-Castro pilots landed in Florida—not because of that undetected flight, but because the radars were finally in operational condition. The Gap-Filler Radars are specially designed to detect aircraft that come in low and slowly. Radars to detect the high- and faster-flying airplanes had long been in operation along the Florida Coast.

The 966th Airborne Early Warning Control Squadron at McCoy Air Force Base, Orlando, Florida, keeps a 24-hour vigil on Cuban military jet aircraft. Radar information is fed to NORAD Headquarters, 2,000 miles away, where a minute-by-minute assessment is made of Cuban military air operations, seven days a week.

CLOSE WATCH ON SPACE

Apart from NORAD's thorough radar coverage of aircraft and missiles, the Space Surveillance web of the U. S. Navy aids in keeping close tabs on all man-made objects orbiting beyond the Earth. SPASUR reports directly to the Space Detection and Tracking System (SPADATS) Operations Control Center at NORAD. The SPADATS Control Center has stored in the memory units of its high-speed electronic computer a description of every known man-made object in orbit. These include fragments of metal and plastic from rockets or satellites that have broken up in space as well as orbiting rocket cases and other debris. SPASUR covers the skies above the basic atmosphere across the entire United States. It has already detected an 8-foot length of thin wire orbiting a hundred-odd miles above the Earth.

The SPADATS Operations Control Center at NORAD, however, does not depend solely on SPASUR for space surveillance. Reporting to the Center are optical-tracking stations equipped with Super-Schmidt-Baker-Nunn cameras that can clearly photograph objects up to a distance out in space of 100,-000 miles. Also cooperating with the space detection network are the radio-tracking and additional optical-tracking devices of the Air Force and the National Aeronautics and Space Administration. The cameras and radio-trackers are spread around the world. All of them supply practically instantaneous data to the Center at Colorado Springs.

The electronic digital computer at the SPADATS Center is in itself a marvel of modern technology. Its memory-core can store more than 32,000 words and provide printed answers to questions at the rate of over 21,000 words per minute. It can make 132,000 additions or subtractions per second as well as

50,000 divisions or multiplications per second. It tirelessly computes the positions and position-changes of every known object in orbit, so that when an unknown appears it can be instantly recognized as such. This up-to-the-second information is constantly displayed on status boards in the SPADATS Control Center and from there is immediately available to the Battle Staff of NORAD's Combat Operations Center.

It was at the main Battle Staff position in the Combat Operations Center, on October 5, 1960, that automatic traces on the BMEWS screen seemed to indicate a ballistic missile attack against the United States by Russia through the radar beams fanning outward from Thule, Greenland.

The BMEWS screen plots the positions of intercontinental ballistic missiles as they come up over the top of the world toward North America. It would also plot the rise of intermediate-range ballistic missiles (IRBMs) if they were launched toward the United Kingdom. To the right of the big BMEWS screen is an even larger screen that displays a map of the entire North American Continent. This main screen gives two kinds of information. It plots the courses of manned aircraft from every direction, and it also predicts impact locations for ICBMs that are first detected on the BMEWS screen. Both screens operate automatically. Both project white ellipses over their respective maps—the BMEWS screen shows the north polar regions and the Soviet Union beyond—to indicate the rise and fall of ICBMs. Within the ellipses alphabetical letters and numbers appear. The letters are the initials of the specific BMEWS site that is detecting the missiles. The numbers indicate the quantity of missiles in the attack. An example would be "T-3," or three missiles located within the area of the ellipse, detected by Thule. "C" and "F" would naturally identify the detection sites as those at Clear, Alaska, and Fylingdales Moor, England. Above the BMEWS screen also is a window with the legend "Minutes To Go." A rapid counter behind the window numerically and visually indicates the amount of time remaining before the first missile impacts on its indicated target. After the impact, the counter automatically rolls back to the time remaining for impact of the second missile, then it rolls back for the third, and so forth. All projections on both screens are controlled by high-speed electronic computers.

The Battle Staff members sit behind a long console facing the screens in a darkened room. The scene resembles, but is much more dramatic than, a cinema screen during an exciting moment in a theatre.

MISSILE ATTACK ON THE U.S.A.

Only four days after the radar site at Thule became operational, the COC Battle Staff members at Colorado Springs were startled out of their routine vigil of the BMEWS screen when a white ellipse abruptly appeared surrounding "T-4." That immediately meant to them that four ICBMs were enroute to the United States. This was indicated by the position of the ellipse over the carefully scaled grid superimposed on the map.

At that moment General Laurence S. Kuter, then Commander-in-Chief of NORAD, was in his staff airplane flying over South Dakota, enroute to Colorado Springs after an inspection tour of facilities in the Central Defense Zone of the United States. His deputy, Canadian Air Marshal C. Roy Slemon, was the delegated man with authority to lift the red and gold telephones from their cradles and by that simple action, perhaps, set into motion a global nuclear holocaust. Within the ellipse, the numbers were changing rapidly: "T-5," "T-10," "T-35." In a matter of seconds, the number of missiles being detected at Thule reached "T-99"—and leveled off. This would be the equivalent of 11 squadrons of America's mightiest ICBM, the TITAN—and the United States has considered a total force of twelve TITAN squadrons to be adequate for all heavy ICBM strategic bombardment. It was indeed a devastatingly massive surprise attack that showed on the BMEWS screen.

But Air Marshal Slemon did not reach for the red and gold

telephones. It took him exactly a minute, in consultation with other members of the Battle Staff, to determine that the situation was a false alarm and that the focal point of the trouble was Thule itself—not missiles, not the communications network.

Certain important information that prevented the attack-alarm from being considered seriously was missing. Five basic elements are required before that gold telephone can be lifted to announce that the United States or our allies are under attack. Only one of these elements was present on the screen: the number of missiles and a static location. No point of impact was indicated on the bigger screen. The counter was not indicating the number of minutes to go before the first missile impacted. Nor was there an indication of a launching point for any of the missiles on the BMEWS screen. Finally, a swift consultation with the intelligence specialists indicated that what was known of Soviet plans and military movements did not jibe with a massive surprise attack at that time.

The real reason for a screen-indication of 99 Russian missiles was pinpointed at Thule in short order. The powerful radar beams from Greenland were reaching the moon, which in rising had attained a position at which the lunar surface reflected them back to Earth. The electronic computer mistook the lunar reflections for reflections characteristic of the body or Re-entry Vehicle of many missiles. The error became immediately apparent when the computer's answers were examined. The computer had been dividing the radar's maximum detection-distance (3,000 miles) into the distance between the antenna and the reflecting source. Since the source, in this case, was roughly 240,-000 miles away, the computer's answer was a very high positive number. Normally, the answer should begin with one, go to fractions, then to negative numbers. If the reflecting source had been missiles from Russia, the radar would have first detected them at 3,000 miles; as they continued toward their target this distance would have diminished with time. The computer, by constantly using 3,000 as its denominator, would have fed lower and lower numbers to the "Minutes To Go" counter at NORAD Headquarters.

The system, in other words, is foolproof—as this "attack" on the United States proved conclusively. No other incident or false alarm has occurred since at any of the BMEWS sites.

When I later mentioned the incident to Lieutenant Colonel Herb Rolph, Assistant Chief of Information at NORAD, he laughed and said, "Up until the time of those moon-reflections, nobody ever thought these radars could be that powerful."

Colonel Rolph, however, did not laugh at Bertrand Russell's description of the incident, from the internationally publicized book, *Has Man A Future?** I read it to him without preliminary comment, just to get his spontaneous reaction. "Once at least," wrote Lord Russell, "the moon was mistaken for a Russian attack and only the accidental interposition of an iceberg which broke communications prevented a retaliatory attack. On all these occasions, the bombers started on their journey. . . ."

The Colonel's reaction was all but instantaneous, as he interrupted me in sheer, incredulous indignation. "That's *entirely* erroneous! There was no such thing as an iceberg interjected in this situation at all! There was no threat whatsoever!" I dislike using exclamation points to punctuate sentences, but in this case they accurately emphasize Colonel Rolph's indignation.

He was equally wrathful when I quoted Lord Russell's accusation that "Several times warning has been given when it turned out that what radar was showing was a flight of geese."

"Negative! Absolutely *not!*" he practically shouted. The Colonel then explained to me that a flock of wild geese *had* flown through one of the doppler cones, or energy fans, of the Mid-Canada Line—*not* BMEWS, which covers much higher altitudes than those at which geese can fly—and had been mistaken for unknown aircraft. But the mistake lasted only several

---

* Bertrand Russell, *Has Man A Future?* (New York: Simon and Schuster, Inc., 1962. Original Edition published in England by the world copyright owner, Penguin Books, Ltd.).

seconds. The Mid-Canada Line employs a series of energy fans, one behind the other, for exactly the purpose of detecting enemy bombers flying low toward the Canadian-United States border. The geese did not penetrate the second group of energy fans, hence could not possibly have been considered to be a fleet of enemy aircraft heading south toward the United States.

The Mid-Canada line may be visualized as a forest of giant, invisible ice cream cones, staggered one behind the other. They are shaped thus by beams of microwave radio energy pointing straight up at the sky. The same effect, on a much smaller scale, can be achieved by pointing a flashlight overhead into the night sky. The flashlight beam is visible electromagnetic energy; the microwave radio beams, also electromagnetic, are invisible. If an airplane flew low through the flashlight beam, reflections could be seen coming back toward the Earth at an angle. The same situation holds true with beams of microwave radio. When there are a number of beams staggered in both horizontal and vertical rows, the reflections that come back to the ground can be received and analyzed to indicate the direction and speed of the reflecting body. As reflecting agents the geese could not have had the speed of even the slowest moving bombers. If their flight pattern, by the most incredible chance, should have taken them southward through all the vertical rows of the Mid-Canada Line, they still could not conceivably have started a war by mistake. Ignoring the dissimilarity of their speed to that of military aircraft, the worst damage they might have done would have been to cause an alert until interceptors of the RCAF Air Defense Command were sent aloft to investigate the "invaders."

DEAD DUCKS VS. MISSILES

In order to be detected at all by a BMEWS site, geese would have to fly directly in front of the tremendous antennae. Before they could cause the slightest alarm, they would be transformed into a flock of "dead ducks," fried crisply by the concentrated source of violent radiation energy emanating from the antennae.

Early in 1962, the BMEWS network was placed under the command of the then newly formed Ninth Aerospace Defense Division of the USAF Air Defense Command. The word "aerospace" is obviously a contraction of the words "aeronautics" and "space." It designates military operations both inside and outside the atmosphere. The Ninth Aerospace Defense Division could be called the farsighted eyes of the Air Defense Command, since its major mission is to detect and warn of space-borne, rather than airborne, threats. Defense against the "aero" portion of "aerospace" is allocated to the highly capable air divisions of the Command. All, of course, are operationally controlled by NORAD.

The Ninth Aerospace Defense Division differs distinctly from the Command's eight air defense divisions. Each of these protects a neatly laid out geographical area of the United States. Responsibilities of the Ninth are global. Some of the locations and equipment within its realm are security-classified. Altogether, it receives reports from more than six hundred space-detection sensors. Headquarters of the Ninth is also at Colorado Springs. Among the six hundred sensors are every known type, optical and radio (which includes radar). About fifty different scientific organizations, military and civilian, compile special tracking data from stations around the world for these reports to the Ninth Aerospace Defense Division. Yet the Division has one other distinct, if somewhat disturbing, difference from its eight complementary air divisions. Its mission and responsibilities are not today involved with actual combat. It has no operational defense weapons for the destruction of hostile space vehicles launched against the Free World.

At the moment, the effectiveness of the Ninth Aerospace Defense Division depends upon its detection and warning capabilities so that if an enemy does attempt a massive surprise attack from space, there will be sufficient time for the Strategic Air Command to get its bombers airborne before they can be destroyed on the ground. The BMEWS network, in the case of long-range ballistic missiles, can give 15 minutes advance warning—and this is time enough at present.

Yet suppose Mr. Khrushchev was not merely boasting when he claimed in March 1962 that the Soviet Union had developed "invulnerable" ballistic missiles that can be launched the long way around the world to avoid the BMEWS radar beams? Suppose the Soviets have developed—as a number of popular, but not official, commentators believe—a terrifying new space satellite that can launch nuclear bombs at chosen targets on the ground as it orbits around the Earth? How can these be detected in sufficient time to avoid catastrophe? Such were the questions that I asked of Colonel Robert Wesley Waltz, not long after he was appointed Commander of the Ninth Aerospace Defense Division.

Colonel Waltz, in his early forties, is a Command Pilot and a veteran of more than 500 hours of combat bomber experience during World War II. He is serious and straightforward. A husky man with grayish hair worn in a crewcut, he is the father of three children. Certainly his personal, in addition to his patriotic, stakes are high for the prevention of war. He was not noticeably disturbed when I asked my leading questions.

Regarding Mr. Khrushchev's long-way-around missile, Colonel Waltz answered: "My opinion is they do not have that capability at the present time. If they did have it—the ability to launch southward and come up at us over the South Pole—then, of course, the present BMEWS sites do not have the capability of detecting that kind of a launch."

"But would any of our tracking stations in the Pacific have that kind of capability?" I asked.

He nodded. "Yes. Some of the tracking stations would. But here again you are faced with a problem. If you didn't know in advance that something had been launched, it would be just chance to detect it passing overhead. As you know, these missiles travel at a tremendous rate of speed. If the tracking radar happened to be pointing in their direction, at the particular time they were coming over, you might get a reading on them."

"Then why," I asked, "do you feel, despite the great payloads the Soviets claim to have placed in orbit, that they do not have a present capability to strike at us from over the South Pole? Some commentators have speculated that the launching of Russian cosmonauts into long-endurance orbits around the Earth automatically suggests that the Soviets *do* have the capability of launching ICBMs at us from the other way around the world. In fact, Mr. Khrushchev himself used Cosmonaut Titov as proof of this."

Colonel Waltz smiled. "You, or those commentators, are now talking more about rocket-engine thrust, or payload-lift capability, than you are about guidance systems. Guidance is of prime importance—and the more distance a missile has to travel, the more chance will there be for error in guidance. There is another consideration—the sacrifice of warning times. As an example: Were the Russians actually to fire a missile over the South Pole—and I think that we would be aware of the actual launch itself—this could provide us with up to an hour-and-a-half warning, rather than the 15-minute warning we would enjoy (if you can call it that) from a missile-launch over the North Pole. So they are sacrificing a great deal if they try to go around through the rear door to come in and hit us. In effect, they would be providing the United States with a much greater lead-time to execute our counterforce strategy."

NUCLEAR BOMBARDMENT SATELLITES

Next I asked for his opinion about the possibility of hostile satellites dropping nuclear bombs on targets in North America. His answer was brief, but full of conviction. "In my own mind, regarding satellites, I believe that the state of the art in research and development has a long way to go. I do not think that the production of a satellite with destructive capability against the North American Continent is possible today. As far as the Soviet Union is concerned, I don't think their state of the art has progressed to that degree."

Nevertheless, I asked Colonel Waltz another leading question. "Someday there may be hostile satellites. What detection methods do you have now—or will have soon—in use to determine whether or not a satellite is hostile?"

"The Air Force and other services have been working on a Satellite Inspector System. Hopefully, within not too long a period we will have the capability of launching an Inspector with the use of a rocket-powered missile. Once it is in orbit, its purpose will be to make contact with the unknown satellite already in orbit and give us visual information by television, or some other kind of read-out information, on where the unknown came from as well as, hopefully, what its intent is.

"In the meantime, we have been maintaining a catalogue of every man-made object in space, so that we have all the known factors. If an unknown appears, we would have to verify that it was not launched by a Free World country. Today, of course, the United States and the USSR are the only two countries that have placed payloads in orbit—so we can rest assured that, at least for now, if something man-made shows up that we cannot identify, it is from the USSR."

"Then your space-detection system is effective," I asked, "efficient enough so that you would know right away when an uncatalogued vehicle appeared?"

"Yes, sir!" the Colonel answered emphatically. "At least we would know in a period of hours."

"Hours? Isn't that a rather long time for detection?"

He shook his head negatively. "The reason I say 'hours' is because of the prime fact that it does take a certain length of time to get an item into orbit. We *would* have the capability of detecting that something *had* been launched. But we would not immediately be able to ascertain that it had actually gone into orbit. Certain information—we call them 'orbital elements' —is required before the computer can establish an orbit. These elements are provided us by our tracking sensors around the world. Otherwise, the launch that we detected immediately could have been a ballistic missile in a test flight, not carrying a satellite payload."

"But how would you know that the missile was on a test flight, rather than being programmed to attack some Free World nation?"

Colonel Waltz smiled again. "The Soviets today are apparently not launching their missiles or orbital satellites from the same location they would have to use in order to launch hostile ICBMs. They launch most of their satellites out over the Pacific —you are probably already aware of this—and from different launching complexes than those that would be required for an ICBM attack against the North American Continent. When they are launching for orbital purposes, they fire their rockets down over China and out across the ocean."

"Well," I asked, "have you detected any of their test flights from positions which *could* be hostile ICBM launching bases?"

"I'm afraid that I can't answer that question."

"Why not? Is the answer classified?"

"Yes. It is classified."

AN "UNDETECTED" SATELLITE

As an interesting aside to Colonel Waltz's last remark, I would like to recount an experience I had in a stubborn attempt to track down a positive answer to a negative question posed by the United Press-International after the Soviets launched the first of their Cosmos series of satellites in an unexpected orbit. According to the UPI story: "The Russian satellite, about which Moscow has given little information, was said to have gone *unobserved* (my emphasis) for two orbits around the earth because it was launched in a direction slightly different from the one favored by the Soviet Government in previous space experiments. The new satellite's orbit is at an angle of 49 degrees from the equator instead of 65 degrees at which the original sputniks made their appearance."

If it were true that a Soviet space vehicle escaped *detection* in the sky for almost 3½ hours, the aerospace defense-alert situation in the Free World could be considered somewhat less than desirable. In fact, it would be downright alarming. Cosmos I, the satellite in question, was launched from the Soviet Union on March 16, 1962. When its orbit was finally established, the period of each of its passes around the world amounted to more than an hour and 40 minutes. The UPI story, with an April 4, 1962, Washington, D.C. dateline, implied that there *was* something wrong with our space-detection systems because Cosmos I had not been detected until sometime during its third pass.

From what I know firsthand of NORAD's highly efficient space-detection network, this just did not seem possible. So I phoned Colorado Springs from New York City and asked a NORAD officer about it. The officer requested "nonattribution." (In simpler words, he did not want to be identified.)

"I'm sorry," he said, "but I can't answer you on that. We have a Department of Defense directive that came down from the President prohibiting us from giving out any details about foreign satellites. Only the civilian Space Administration can give you that information."

"Isn't that *crazy?*" I exclaimed.

"We think so." He paused. "But I *can* tell you this. Everyone here would be very seriously concerned if we missed out on something like that."

"*Were* you concerned?"

"No comment," he said lightly and laughed. "You'll have to get in touch with NASA. You might get the real information from them."

It was a Friday evening, already after workaday hours on the East Coast. I wouldn't be able to talk with anyone at NASA until Monday morning—and I *was* anxious to have my questions answered. I mentioned this to the officer. He gave me the telephone number of the night-duty man in the satellite-tracking section of the Goddard Space Flight Center at Greenbelt, Maryland. "Maybe if you catch this guy off guard, he'll tell you what you want to know," said my NORAD informant.

I phoned Greenbelt and explained to the night-duty man on

tracking that a certain officer at NORAD had given me his number. I then read him excerpts of the UPI story. "Do you recall the incident?" I asked.

"I certainly do," he said. "Why didn't Colonel ——— give you the answers? He knows as much as we do about it."

This forced me to explain that NORAD had received a directive prohibiting them from releasing such information.

"We have the same directive," the duty man said. "Only the Information Office of NASA can release that information."

I said, "Look, knowing the kinds of tracking equipment we have spaced around the world, I can't *believe* that we couldn't catch that Soviet satellite on its first orbit!"

He laughed, in a manner similar to that of the NORAD officer. "I know *exactly* how you feel! Wish I could tell you. We can't. We don't have the authority to release that information. Sorry. You'll have to try catching the Information people on Monday."

Monday morning I phoned the Office of Public Information at NASA's Goddard Space Flight Center and spoke with a specialist in satellite-tracking information, who also did not want to be named. He was trying to be as helpful as the others—and like the others, was helpless. After I quoted from the UPI story and asked him, "Is that true?" his first words were:

"I can neither confirm nor deny that report. But let me say this: I don't believe everything I read in the papers. Do you?"

"Heck no!" I answered. "But that's just the point. This story implied—more than implied, stated—that there was a breach in United States space-detection systems for defense."

"Well, I can tell you one thing," he said. "When they (the Russians) launch something—we know it."

"Then, in a general way, could you at least tell me whether the UPI reporter was accurate?"

"This gets a little sticky," he retorted. "Let me just add— that he probably didn't know all the facts."

"You're implying then that there was a lot more to this situation than what appeared in the newspapers?"

"Now you're getting into a *quite* sticky area," said he. "You know when the DoD (Department of Defense) is involved, they don't want certain people to know the accuracy of our detection devices or even the locations of some of these devices. Too much detailed information released on tracking objects in space would tip off those certain people to things the DoD doesn't want them to know about American tracking equipment. We're allowed to give some information—but not much."

Which turns my pursuit of a positive answer right around and deposits it in a deep moat that guards intelligence techniques from the man in the street. It is called "The Need to Know." I did not have "the need to know." The UPI reporter did not have that need either. Nor do you, the reader, have it. This is why I have quoted verbatim my telephone interviews on the subject—so that you could infer your own conclusions about the episode.

SURVEILLANCE TO THE MOON

One thing is certain, however, about the space-detection aspects of NORAD. The Ninth Aerospace Division is not trusting the future to take care of itself. Two new detection projects are presently being researched and developed by the Air Force Systems Command for ultimate operational use by the SPADATS Control Center. One of these is a surveillance network that will continuously and automatically survey all of cis-lunar space (the area of space that extends from the Earth to the moon). The network does not have a name as yet, but it is being developed at the Space Track Research and Development Facility of the Electronic Systems Division of the Systems Command in Massachusetts. Research was begun at the request of NORAD.

According to Dr. Eberhard W. Wahl, acting chief scientist on the project, "With the technical application of astronomy to the specific purpose of man-made satellite surveillance, all of the space between here and the moon will get a really thorough going-over. If there is anything of any size between here and the moon, we will find it and track it."

The new system will combine powerful optical telescopes, photosensitive surfaces, microwave radio and high-speed data-correlation techniques. Dr. Wahl also said, "We will first have to find and track any natural moonlets that may exist, because until we establish an inventory of everything in orbit out there, we cannot tell if something has been added.

"It would be relatively easy to determine whether the detected object were a natural moonlet or a man-made one," Dr. Wahl elaborated. "Natural moonlets would be heavy chunks of rock, whereas man-made satellites are normally hollow, instrument-carrying objects.

"In either case, the position and orbit of any satellite (natural or unnatural) would be logged in so that if an unannounced satellite—not sent up by the United States—were discovered, SPADATS could say with certainty, 'This is a natural moonlet' or 'This is a foreign satellite.'"

Dr. Wahl's almost casual, if graphic, descriptions of the purpose of this new space-surveillance system underplay the technological imaginativeness and daring of the total concept. For inherent in the vastness of this system, in its optical and electronic engineering complexity, are problems that transcend those encountered in the development of BMEWS. Yet it is precisely such ambitious boldness and ingenuity that keep the enemy in his place, that force him to believe in our strength and thus discourage him from attempting aggressive acts on the global or nuclear scale.

The second new space-detection project is almost equally revolutionary. It is an electronically guided radar system that will be able to sweep the skies in all directions at nearly the speed of light. Technically, it is called a "phased array radar." The Air Force official announcement of its development stated that it "can be directed to a desired position much faster than is possible with the ponderous mechanical antennae in common usage today. This radar technique permits the use of a number of duplicate transmitters and receivers to track many widely separated targets concurrently at high speed.

"This multiple-target capability with electronic steering can be programmed by a computer at extremely high speeds, thus greatly enhancing the space-tracking and detection system's ability to detect, track, identify and catalogue all man-made satellites."

In less restrained words than those of the official announcement, the new radar system will be capable of discovering, locking onto and tracking dozens of satellites at the same time. It will reduce to practically zero the possibility of a massive surprise attack from orbital vehicles. Such an attack, of course, is presently far beyond the borders of probability—but who can say with absolute conviction that a potential enemy might not achieve an unexpected technological breakthrough in the near future to make this "science-fiction" type of attack possible?

The conventional tracking radars locate and lock onto an object, or target, by means of the mechanical rotation of their usually dish-shaped antennae. Signals are transmitted in pulses, or as spurts of microwave radio energy. The spurts are synchronized so that when they strike a target and are reflected back toward the rotating antenna, they will be received during the intervals between spurts and can thus be detected without being blocked by outgoing spurts of signals. Small radar "dishes" on aircraft rotate to sweep the skies about once every 15 seconds. The larger antennae, because they are also mechanical, rotate more slowly. At the BMEWS sites, the tracking radar antennae are about 84 feet in diameter. Their job is tracking only and not detection, which, except for the Fylingdales Moor site, is reserved for the giant football-field-size antennae. These detection antennae are fixed, not rotated. The new system would have an array, or planned grouping, of huge fixed antennae that would combine both detection and tracking of objects in space. Spurts of transmitted energy could be quickly shifted electronically from one antenna in the group to another in order to sweep 360 degrees of the sky in less time than it takes a small conventional radar antenna to rotate through 24 degrees.

DISCOURAGING ENEMY SATELLITE-BORNE ATTACK

When the new electronically steered radar system becomes operational, it could by its very presence discourage an enemy from pursuing research and development programs aimed at the massive surprise attack concept through the use of space satellites carrying nuclear weapons.

The deterrent power of adequate defense-alarm systems should never be underrated. Colonel Barney Oldfield, former Chief of Information at NORAD, highlighted this point during a speech he gave before the Aviation/Space Writers Association at Fort Worth, Texas, 8 months before his retirement in October 1962. In two brief paragraphs, he smartly tacked down the situation.

"He [Secretary of Defense McNamara] said we cannot provide an absolute defense against unfriendly forces which might approach the North American Continent," commented Colonel Oldfield, "but he did say that we have a highly effective system against manned bomber attack (and here I quote directly) 'particularly since the Soviet Union did not build the large manned bomber force anticipated many years ago by the planners of the system' end quote.

"Lest this be interpreted as a planning error, let me say that *any defensive force formidable enough to discourage a production line is a pretty good expenditure of effort and money.*" (The italics are mine.)

Colonel Oldfield, of course, was referring not only to North America's detection-alarm systems but also to the combat weapon systems that defend our continent. Yet detection-alarm systems by themselves are a mighty part of the Free World's deterrent strength, since NORAD and SAC are interdependent military commands. While NORAD, through the Air Defense Command, would physically defend our continent if an alarm proved to be real, SAC with its deadly bombers and lethal long-range missiles would be able to cripple an enemy thoroughly if he dared to attack from *any* level of the aerospace realm. Sufficient warning time makes this possible. And sufficient warning time results *only* from advanced detection-alarm systems. I have stated this previously. It cannot be said too often.

Still, how vulnerable is the North American Continent to an enemy aerospace attack?

That was my first question when I interviewed General Robert Merrill Lee, then Commander of the USAF Air Defense Command, the major combat arm of NORAD. Not long after I spoke with him, he was given a position of even higher authority as Air Deputy to the Supreme Allied Commander in Europe. General Lee is a tall, rangy man in his early fifties, a slow-speaking, unperturbed New Englander who nevertheless is quickwitted and precisely organized. He earned his four stars through hard work in positions of considerable responsibility, having served as Deputy Commanding General for Operations, Ninth Air Force; Chief of Staff, Tactical Air Command; Deputy Chief of Staff for Operations, Headquarters USAF; Commander of the Fourth Allied Tactical Air Force (the largest in NATO); Chief of Staff for both the United Nations Command and the United States Forces in Korea. For two-and-a-quarter years he was Commander of the Air Defense Command. His important decorations are too numerous for mention. He came up the long way, from the temporary rank of Second Lieutenant, which was made a permanent rank in June 1931. Since August 1, 1963, he has been a four-star general. Born in a small New Hampshire town, he is married to an Alabama girl. They have three sons. His stake in maintaining world peace is thus as great as that of Colonel Waltz.

His answer to my first question was: "There is a lot of opinion on this subject—and a good share of it is uninformed." He was leaning back in a leather-upholstered chair, casually smoking a cigarette. The microphone of my tape-recorder was sitting in a big ashtray on a stand in front of him. He managed always to flick the ashes into the tray without having them fall near the microphone and without uncrossing his long legs. It typified his self-assured, unexcitable temperament. We were talking in his large, neat Headquarters office of the time at Colorado Springs. He thoughtfully considered the next statement of his answer, then continued.

"Much of the negative thinking regarding aerospace defense arises, I believe, from an idea widely circulated some years ago —that the best any aerospace defense force could do would be to knock down about 30 per cent of an invading bomber fleet. In some quarters, this notion still seems to be circulating today.

"The result of this misconception—and it *is* a misconception —has been the growth of a more or less fatalistic attitude about air attack in the atomic age. The feeling seems to be that while our defenses can get some of the invaders, the rest of them will get us, so why spend money on air defenses.

"I personally would like to bury this misconception for all time. It is not only false—it is dangerous to the security of this nation."

"Why is it dangerous?" was a logical next question.

"As simply as I can put it," he said, "both deterrence of war and victory in the event of war—or war-winning capability— depend importantly on aerospace defense to complement our offensive might. If our defenses are weak, then we might neither deter war nor win it.

"We might not deter it because without defenses we are offering the enemy the opportunity to apply his weapons without defensive opposition. *This nation simply could not afford to give an enemy the tremendous advantage of unopposed nuclear attack.*

"Conversely, if an aggressor *knows* he *must* lose considerably more bombers than he can get through, he's going to think— not twice—but long and seriously before accepting such prohibitive odds. His loss factor today is largely the sum of the ability of our strategic striking forces to attack hostile targets at their source *plus* that portion of his attacking force destroyed by our defensive forces.

"Therefore, credible deterrence arises from the combined capability of our offensive and defensive forces to destroy the attacking force. Neither, by itself, can be called a deterrent force. This is why it is dangerous to national security to say, 'Why spend the money?'

"All of our extensive aerospace defense resources—radars, manned interceptors, missiles and the command and control communications, including BMEWS, provided by my command for instantaneous reporting to NORAD—guard an area of some 10½ million square miles. They represent a capital investment of approximately 8 billion dollars. It's a cheap price to pay for deterring war."

"But what if deterrence fails?" I asked. "I know of many people, highly intelligent people, who using their best logic have arrived at the certainty that deterrence *must* fail, is fated to fail."

SURVIVAL AND RECOVERY

General Lee barely smiled. He did not try to belabor the point by contesting it. He merely said: "In such a situation, the job of limiting damage to our country is largely in the hands of our defensive forces. If they have what it takes to do the job, they can reduce significantly the amount of damage we would suffer. If they do not have what it takes, then the job of recovering from a nuclear war will be far more difficult. Civil defense is digging the cellar. But aerospace defense is building the roof."

"Yet how effective *today*, during the 1963-64 period, say, is our aerospace defense system?"

"With the aerospace forces existing today," he said, "we can severely cripple an aggressor's striking power the first time he comes over, thereby minimizing, if not destroying, his capability for repeated attacks. Meanwhile, at his own strike bases, he is being struck by our own long-range strategic forces. In other words, with today's aerospace capability, we could survive and recover—without it, we could not.

"This fact, *I am sure*, is well known in the planning center of any potential aggressor."

"Then," I asked, "it is this certain knowledge that discourages an enemy from even planning a massive surprise attack? He *knows* in advance that it would not succeed?"

General Lee nodded.

"Let me ask one more question. How do you deter an enemy from an aggressive action through outer space—if you have no counteractive weapons that can destroy his before they hit their targets?"

"That's a good question. In aerospace defense we perform five basic functions: surveillance, detection, identification, interception and destruction. As regards the air-breathing threat—principally bombers—we can *and are* performing all of these functions well. In space defense, our position is not so good. We are now performing the first three—surveillance, detection and identification—but we do not presently have an intercept and destruct capability.

"Looking at the other side of the coin, I see no reason to be pessimistic about our ability to attain the other two elements of active space defense. We have built our present capability in aerospace defense because we had the national will to do so. I am confident that the national will to go the rest of the way is just as strong.

"One by one, we are closing the doors to a potential aggressor. With our present space-surveillance capability, and with our Ballistic Missile Early Warning System, we have halfway shut the space door. As for the rest of the job, I can only say: We can, we must *and* we will."

General Lee was referring most immediately to the NIKE-ZEUS antimissile missile system. The ZEUS had been the subject of some controversy because of its high cost and also because a number of influential persons felt that it would be impossible to develop a system that could intercept a target as small as a nuclear-charged Re-entry Vehicle plunging down through the Earth's atmosphere at an average speed of 16,000 miles an hour. Five months after I spoke with General Lee, the ZEUS proved that the "impossible" could be done. On July 19, 1962, at 9:45 A.M., Pacific Daylight Time, a NIKE-ZEUS successfully intercepted the Re-entry Vehicle of an ATLAS Intercontinental Ballistic Missile about 600 miles above Kwajalein Island. The RV was plummeting toward the lower atmosphere at 16,000 miles per hour. The ICBM that ejected it had been launched approximately 15 minutes earlier from Vandenberg Air Force Base in California, some 4,500 miles away. American science and technology had again overturned the applecart of convention.

When I heard about the amazing success of the NIKE-ZEUS-ATLAS test, it reminded me of General Lee's parting words, as we shook hands. "I am convinced," he said, "that the nation which first achieves an effective ballistic missile defense, will have acquired a significant military advantage. It is up to all of us to see to it that *that* nation is the United States of America."

Now it appears that *that* nation will be the United States of America. Except that 3 days before the successful ZEUS test, Nikita Khrushchev told members of the American Society of Newspaper Editors in Moscow: "I am not boasting, but we actually have a global rocket which cannot be destroyed by any antirocket means, and I know, if anybody does, what antirocket means are, because we do have them. You can say our rocket hits a fly in outer space."

HOW HONEST WAS KHRUSHCHEV?

Was Russian Premier N. S. Khrushchev telling the whole truth, or was he merely fabricating propaganda for leading members of the American Press? The answer to that question can be inferred from a subtly caustic remark made by United States Defense Secretary Robert McNamara as he announced the successful NIKE-ZEUS test over the Pacific. "The test," said Mr. McNamara, "evidences the extensive and continuing nature of the United States program to understand the capabilities and limitations of antimissile systems. It shows that we speak of such matters from knowledge."

Speaking also from knowledge of this subject, just before he retired as Commander-in-Chief of NORAD on July 31, 1962, was General Laurence Sherman Kuter. He said: "One does not have to be a military genius to see what will happen to our capability to deter if the Soviets believe that they have an anti-intercontinental ballistic missile system which will stop an acceptable proportion of our missiles and we have no means of stopping any of theirs.

"I know that we have no system for area defense against the ICBM except in early research and development, and that only the Army's NIKE-ZEUS could possibly be deployed for operation as early as 1966.

"I believe that we have no alternative other than putting NIKE-ZEUS into operation, fully realizing that 4 years and perhaps 10 billion dollars are involved."

The NIKE-ZEUS anti-ICBM weapon system was conceived for terminal defense, concerned with the point in space from which an ICBM Re-entry Vehicle begins to drop toward its target, rather than for area defense, as mentioned by General Kuter. Area defense covers a much wider territory, or a good part of the range of an ICBM enroute to the terminal point. In other words, General Kuter was saying that the United States has more advanced anti-ICBM systems in the beginning research and development stages, but that ZEUS has gone far past these stages and a concerted effort must be made to place it in operation.

As of June 1963, more than 50 per cent of the ZEUS research and development tests were highly successful. An additional 25 per cent were partially successful in meeting test objectives. Among the fully successful tests at intercontinental range was the ZEUS interception of an RV ejected from a TITAN ICBM, in addition to its earlier interception of an ATLAS RV.

However, the original NIKE-ZEUS requirements were conceived during a period when little thought was given to the possibility of an enemy using decoys to mislead an anti-ICBM missile electronically. And although the ZEUS was already the fastest air-defense missile in the Free World, serious defense planners felt that the program should be redirected to bring it up to date—not only in terms of a capability for sharper discrimination against decoys, but also in terms of an even quicker reaction time. In January of 1963, Secretary of Defense Robert Mc-Namara announced the start of the redirected program as "NIKE-X." By March 28 of the same year, new contracts were announced by the U. S. Army for the development not only of NIKE-X—which incorporates an advanced radar system with the capability of simultaneous acquisition, interpretation and tracking of many objects in space—but also for the development of a totally new anti-ICBM missile with extremely high acceleration, popularly called SPRINT.

The SPRINT missile does not replace but complements the ZEUS in the overall system. Although smaller and lighter than the ZEUS, it will be able to reach and destroy enemy targets much faster. Continuing tests with the original ZEUS system are supplying valuable data toward the development of NIKE-X. Over 40 industrial contractors were reviewed in the Fall of 1962 by Western Electric (prime contractor for NIKE-X) and the Department of Defense, to determine the three with the best technological capabilities for successfully developing the SPRINT anti-missile missile. The three chosen—Douglas Aircraft, North American Aviation and the Martin-Orlando Division of Martin Marietta Corporation—were awarded paid 120-day study contracts to determine the best engineering proposal from among them. Martin-Orlando won the ultimate contract to produce the SPRINT as subcontractor to Bell Telephone Laboratories, project manager on NIKE-X. In a real sense, Martin Marietta was a "dark horse" winner, for Douglas Aircraft had had considerable experience with the ZEUS missile as well as with the NIKE-AJAX and NIKE-HERCULES air-defense missiles. Douglas was thus the "favorite." But Martin-Orlando had been quietly acquiring experience with some of the most advanced solid-fuel missiles in the Free World and had the engineering team on hand to produce the best proposal.

Yet despite all this, the original NIKE-ZEUS might well have been dropped as a project, thereby leaving the United States without the immediate hope of any anti-ICBM defense, if it had not been for the continual urgent insistence of a small group of men like General Laurence Sherman Kuter.

During his 3 years as Commander-in-Chief of NORAD, General Kuter made an almost continuously persistent plea for the urgency of a stepped-up development program on the NIKE-ZEUS system. He had many formidable opponents, but this never stopped him. He sincerely felt that the future security of the Free World depended on such a program.

Some months before he retired, I had an excellent opportunity to speak at great length with General Kuter. With his kind permission, I accompanied him in his staff airplane on a flight from NORAD Headquarters at Colorado Springs to Stewart Air Force Base, about 70 miles north of New York City. During the 4-hour and 50-minute flight, I was able to talk with him informally for about 3 hours. Our major subject was: How vulnerable is the North American Continent to enemy attack by either aircraft or missiles—and what is being done to plug existing loopholes?

General Kuter's vast background of experience encompasses the diplomatic and political fields as well as the military. By Presidential Order in 1946, he was appointed the United States representative to help set up the Provisional International Aviation Organization. He continued the following year with the official rank of Minister when the organization became permanent as the International Civil Aviation Organization. He represented the Air Force at the United States-United Kingdom Bilateral Air Conference in Bermuda, aided in the negotiation of an agreement with Portugal and was Commander of the Air University, where he raised the status of the Air Command and Staff School to college level. When the Air Force was still a part of the Army, he was Chief of Staff for the great visionary General, "Hap" Arnold. After General Arnold became suddenly and seriously ill, General Kuter was designated as his personal representative at the historic Yalta and Malta Conferences. Just before he became Commander-in-Chief of NORAD, General Kuter had been Commander-in-Chief of the Pacific Air Forces.

He is a rated Command Pilot with more than 8,000 flying hours and has flown around the world eight times. Obviously he is a man highly cultivated in the ways of international affairs and policy as well as being experienced in almost every aspect of military air combat and strategy.

Regarding the latter, I asked him: "Does the Red Air Force have a bomber in-flight refueling capability that is as advanced and efficient as ours?"

"I don't know whether anyone can answer that," he said. "They've practiced extensively for many years. I've watched them practice myself, by radar in the Far East. Our radar stations throughout the world observe them doing this all the time."

"How do their long-range bombers compare with ours?"

"Well, the range of our B-52 greatly exceeds that of the Bison (Russia's comparable jet bomber)—but their big turboprop bomber, the Bear, has a greater range than the B-52. Of course, it flies slower and lower."

"Then what chance has the Bear of getting through our defenses, since it obviously has the range to reach us?"

General Kuter shook his head emphatically. "They'd be the easiest target we'd ever meet!" He shifted his inordinately tall, big-boned frame in the narrow sofa-like seat across the table from me. "On the other hand," he continued slowly, "they would make good missile-launching platforms from a distance. They wouldn't have to present themselves to our combat defenses. They could stand off and launch missiles like our HOUND DOG."

CAN STAND-OFF MISSILES GET THROUGH?

"In that case," I persisted, "what chance would the missiles have of getting through?"

He hardly pondered the answer. "Missiles like that are small and fast—but the NIKE-HERCULES has an *unquestioned* capability to destroy supersonic air-breathing, or HOUND DOG-type missiles."

The NIKE-HERCULES, as distinguished from the anti-

ICBM NIKE-ZEUS, is a supersonic antiaircraft missile developed by the Army. In many flight tests at the White Sands Missile Range in New Mexico it has intercepted and destroyed infallibly both bomber-type aircraft and short-range missiles. HERCULES batteries ring key cities and other strategic target areas of the United States.

"But how about the faster hypersonic SKYBOLT-type air-launched missiles?" I next asked General Kuter. "Could the NIKE-HERCULES get these?"

"The best defense against these ballistic penetration missiles is to kill the carrier," he answered, "whether it's an airplane or a submarine. You don't attempt to ward off bullets one at a time. You go out and get the gun, destroy it."

Since my interview with General Kuter the United States Department of Defense has dropped the SKYBOLT development program for reasons of economy. On the other hand, the Kremlin might not be equally preoccupied with saving money where SKYBOLT-type missiles were concerned, so my next question still has validity.

"What chance do we have for doing just that? If enemy bombers or submarines stay far enough out from our coasts and fire ballistic missiles at us, how do we stop them?"

"Regarding submarines, the Navy has some highly classified projects to detect them in time and destroy them if they prove to be hostile. The Air Force BOMARC missile has a range of 400 nautical miles, is fully operational, and could get many of the bombers. But there is an urgent need for a long-range manned interceptor, such as the F-108. Today, however, there is no program for the production of this type of interceptor."

"Why not?"

"It was dropped for official reasons. I still believe that it is the prime requirement today for one major aspect of defense against manned bombers."

"But are our defense forces sufficiently reliable and varied to frustrate an enemy attempt at a sneak attack upon North America today—and in the foreseeable future?"

"In my opinion," said General Kuter, "the likelihood of the success of a sneak attack by conventional bombing is sufficiently remote to make it extremely unlikely. It would be too expensive for the enemy, in terms of loss and retaliation. A sneak missile attack would be several times better for him—that is, by missiles like HOUND DOG and SKYBOLT. But a *sneak* attack by such missiles is *extremely* unlikely also. A massive surprise missile attack by ICBM would have to come through the BMEWS system—which is a highly reliable system. So the sneak aspects disappear, wouldn't help an enemy. To sneak in, he would have to use small forces on the pretext that they had wandered off course—or were launched by accident. Our retaliation would be massive to his puny effort."

"How do we know that Russia has the kind of stand-off missiles you mentioned?"

His answer was simple. "Whether or not the Soviet Union has these types of missiles today, we must be prepared to meet such a threat for the future."

TODAY'S BIGGEST THREAT

"What would you say was the biggest threat from the enemy today—missiles or manned aircraft?"

"Today, the biggest threat is the manned bomber. It is equally clear that the time is not far off in the future when the graph will change, the curves will cross—and the biggest threat then will be a missile. But long after those curves have crossed, although the manned bomber will then be a lesser threat, it will still be a fatal threat.

"The missile is an additional, not a replacement, threat. The cannon never absolutely replaced the musket.

"We will always have a requirement to police what we define as our airspace, in both the functions of peace or war. And such policing will require men in high-performance supersonic aircraft—as long as men can fly. Obviously, with present technology, it would be no great problem to produce a Mach 6 (six times the speed of sound) manned interceptor for future policing."

"But General Kuter, how do you determine what a future threat will be?"

"That is purely in the realm of planning. From a planning viewpoint, all areas of possible attack are considered and analyzed in terms of what we know about the enemy and in terms of the rate of progress in present technology. All logical future threats are covered by plans."

"Then, speaking of the future, do the flights around the world of the Russian cosmonauts prove that the Soviet Union has a capability to strike us from satellites carrying heavy thermonuclear weapons?"

The General shook his head. "No, you couldn't say that they prove the Soviet Union has that capacity. The cosmonauts have demonstrated only that Russia has the capacity to lift great weight into space. However, the sophistication of control of their spacecraft, apparently demonstrated early in the game by Gagarin and Titov, suggests that the Russians someday could strike at selected targets from space, utilizing satellites with weapons of great nuclear strength." General Kuter paused before emphasizing his next point. "I certainly dont want to imply those satellites would be carrying 100-megaton weapons. Weapons like that involve much heavier weights than could be tugged along by satellites for a long, long time to come."

As a follow-up question, I asked, "What is your personal reaction to Khrushchev's statement that he has a 'Sword of Damocles' hanging over the United States—his 100-megaton bomb?"

"My reaction to that was: he was guilty of trite oratory."

General Kuter's elegant disdain of Mr. Khrushchev's boasting was undoubtedly based on intelligence information, since the General, as Commander-in-Chief of NORAD, had the need to know all available data on Soviet weapons that might be employed in an attack against the North American Continent.

Since my interview with General Kuter, of course, the Soviets have announced the launching of cosmonauts other than Gagarin and Titov. Their most spectacularly notable announcement concerned the orbiting of a man and the world's first space-woman about two days apart. These cosmonauts were said to be riding in the satellites Vostok IV and Vostok V very close together in the same general orbit, for purposes of testing rendezvous techniques—that is, to pull up alongside each other in space for the transfer of fuel or cargo. The first woman in orbit was Junior Lieutenant Valentina Tereshkova, who claimed to have circled the earth 48 times in almost three days of travel. Her cosmic male companion was Lt. Colonel Valery Bykovsky. It was officially stated that he rode his capsule through space during 81 orbits—for five days minus less than an hour. According to the announcement, they came within three miles of each other at one point. Whether or not the Soviets have achieved their stated purposes with any of the cosmonauts, the words of General Kuter still apply strongly to the defense of North America: "We must be prepared to meet such a threat for the future." Some day, Russian cosmonauts *may* be able to rendezvous in space for the transfer of nuclear-weapon segments, put these together as they orbit and drop them on selected targets in the Free World. The chances of their being able to do this for the next several decades are highly improbable. The chances that they would do it if they could are all but impossible, since striking three or four targets in the Free World would only cause the USSR to be subjected to an insupportable retaliatory attack. A massive surprise attack by satellite is impossible for several reasons, the two most obvious being that it would require launching of a large number of satellites in sequence or pre-existence of a big network of satellites already in established orbits. Either way, the element of surprise would be lost. The satellites would be swiftly detected and sharply watched. Precautions would instantly be effected. Retaliation on a massive scale would be assured. Chapter 7 will recount future plans of the United States to counter a nuclear threat from outer space.

"Yet nuclear weapons are not the only threat to America," I told General Kuter and asked: "What defense do we have against chemical and germ warfare as well as against sabotage?"

"That is out of my province," he answered. "I think you ought to talk with J. Edgar Hoover on that question. The FBI has the authority and the experience to answer it."

A week later I was in Washington, D.C., trying to obtain an appointment with the Director of the FBI. I was reluctantly denied a personal interview with Mr. Hoover. However, I *was* able to talk several times with Inspector Robert Wick, the FBI officer who, close to Mr. Hoover, acted as my liaison. In addition to a number of formal statements by Mr. Hoover given to me for quotation, the conversations I had with Inspector Wick are particularly instructive.

He had requested that I submit my specific questions in written form so that Mr. Hoover could study them. He later apologized because they could not be answered. "We wanted to help you develop the theme for your book," he said. "In fact, Mr. Hoover and several of us worked out a series of answers for you. But after considering them carefully and submitting them through the various departments here, it was unanimously decided that even the most general statements would give aid and comfort to the enemy.

"There are just too many complex facets involved. The Litvinov Agreement of 1933, for example, which gives the Soviet Union diplomatic immunity."

"But can't you say *anything?*" I asked. "The main point of my book is to reassure the average American that he and his nation are as secure as modern science, human vigilance and the intense dedication of anonymous hundreds of thousands of dedicated persons can make them."

Inspector Wick's answer: "Mr. Hoover once said that during World War II there was no single case of enemy-directed sabotage that was successful."

"That implies there were attempts at sabotage. How many, in just round numbers?"

"Sorry," he said, "the number of attempts is classified."

"Well, at least could you say that today the FBI surveillance of sabotage possibilities is as good as, or better or worse than it was then?"

UNRELENTING INTENSIVE SURVEILLANCE

Inspector Wick started his answer slowly but gained momentum. "The FBI is charged with the responsibility of maintaining internal security of the United States. You hear people talking about the 'Cold War.' Believe me, there's no such thing! It's war. Period! Our surveillance today has not lessened *one bit* since the end of World War II—if anything, it's on a higher level of efficiency. It is a *constant, unrelenting,* around-the-clock intensive surveillance of all Soviet attempts at espionage and sabotage. And I would like to make clear: not only are the Soviets and their supporters in this country under such surveillance —but this also includes the satellite nations, along with their official *and* unofficial representatives. For example, the Czechoslovakian Embassy gathers and ships truckloads of technical papers and books by diplomatic pouch back to Russia. Now this is all right. We can't stop them if the technical material is unclassified. But I'm giving you an example: the FBI *is* aware they're doing this, among other things."

"You mentioned 'diplomatic pouch.' Wouldn't it be possible to smuggle into this country by diplomatic pouch in piecemeal fashion the parts of nuclear bombs? Or even bacteria or chemicals that would generate gases to knock out people guarding strategic military installations? How would we combat a surprise attack from inside our own country? The agreement on diplomatic immunity applies to the pouches also, doesn't it?"

"Yes, it does," said Inspector Wick. "And there are certain pouches that might conceivably carry the things you mention. But although parts of a nuclear device might be brought into this country, we have certain techniques that make this *very* unlikely. The same thing applies to bacteriological and chemical attempts at sabotage. We have our methods of detection without breaking the regulations of diplomatic immunity."

"How closely does the FBI work with other intelligence agencies of the Government, both military and civilian?"

"As a daily routine, we supply intelligence information to the White House and the Department of Defense. This is an up-to-the-minute daily report. It's a complex job because the situation is complex. There is the espionage done by diplomatic representatives—of which there are many—of the Soviet Union and its satellites. Even the chauffeurs and doormen of their various embassies participate in espionage. This is the immune official approach. But also included in the espionage effort are the overt subversive types. Then there are the members of the United States Communist Party—small as they are in number, in a critical situation they would be ready to do sabotage. That's about all I can tell you without compromising the FBI."

I thanked Inspector Wick for telling me as much as he did.

By now, the reader should have a reasonably long inside view of the scope, alertness and efficiency of North America's defense effort. But the panorama nevertheless is incomplete without a few necessary details about the combat aspects of NORAD.

Just as SAC has a concisely organized plan for global offense-in-depth, so does NORAD have that exact kind of plan in terms of area defense. Area defense-in-depth was described for me by Colonel Victor Wegenhoft, Chief of the Advance Plans Division, Office of the Deputy Chief of Staff/Plans, at Air Defense Command Headquarters. He summarized it briefly: "We let the enemy know that we're going to strike him from as far out as we can hit him—and keep hitting him all along the route, until we destroy him. Not many of an aggressor's bombers, I am sure, would get through the total profile to their targets."

I asked him to explain "profile."

"Simply," he said, "it is the route, the flight path, from an enemy's home base to a potential target, wherever that may be. But it is really not so simple because it requires a mixed family, a great variety, of defense weapons in sufficient number with sufficient destructive power to stop that enemy. We must engage the enemy as far out as possible and continue the tempo of our counterattack as he moves closer and closer to the target point—and different portions of the profile require different types of weapons."

"Apparently, then, you have a sufficient variety and number of defense weapons to do the job—from your remark about not many of an aggressor's bombers being able to get through?"

"Oh, yes. In fact, our manned interceptors are almost entirely supersonic. Their routes to the target aircraft are calculated automatically by electronics and their air-to-air missiles are self-guided electronically. Those missiles have nuclear as well as high-explosive warheads. The ground-to-air missiles are also electronically guided and may be also armed with nuclear warheads.

"There is no doubt in my mind that the dollars spent on air defense have more than achieved their objectives. Our defense system, in being against manned enemy bombers, has been developed to a high state of readiness.

"But of course we must continue to improve our air defenses as required by changes in enemy tactics and weapon capabilities. For example, we may soon have to face the idea of enemy bombers employing long-range air-to-surface missiles. When that enemy capability arrives, we must be ready for it by being able to reach out still farther at faster speeds so that we can kill the bomber before it is in a position to launch such missiles."

"Would your area defense profile concept," I asked, "also apply to long-range ICBMs and hostile satellites as well as to manned bombers?"

NO ACTIVE DEFENSE AGAINST SPACE

He nodded. "Except that we have no active defense weapons yet to combat those. Planning the military capabilities needed to defend against enemy aerospace threats of this nature is the function of my job here, as well as the job of others."

"What do you have in the works now for that purpose, apart from the NIKE-X and the Satellite Inspector, which I already know about?"

"We have several projects in the planning stage or beyond," said Colonel Wegenhoft. "For instance, in keeping with our concept of engaging the enemy as far out as possible, we are investigating ways to neutralize a hostile long-range ballistic missile during the boost or mid-course phases of its attack profile. Also under consideration are methods to improve our warning times as well as to provide an active defense against hostile space vehicles."

"Will such advanced systems as you suggest be ready in time to meet the threats they are planned to conquer?"

"The threat of an ICBM attack is facing us today. Against this missile threat, we have a warning capability—but no active defense. However, difficult as the problem is, we believe that an effective active defense can be achieved against ballistic missiles as well as other threats from space."

Earlier I had talked at some length with Colonel Wegenhoft's boss about the more "prosaic" threat from nuclear-bomb-carrying enemy aircraft. This man, Major General Arthur C. Agan, Jr., is Deputy Chief of Staff for Plans at the USAF Air Defense Command Headquarters. His experience with fighter and bomber tactics is firsthand and considerable. During World War II, he was one of five men chosen to write the procedures for the combined bomber offensive in Europe. His skill and experience are so well trusted that he was also chosen to be Commander of the Fighter Escort that flew a protective cover for President Franklin Delano Roosevelt when FDR traveled to Yalta in the Soviet Crimea to attend the historic conference with Stalin. I asked General Agan the following questions.

"Why are nuclear weapons needed for attack against enemy bombers? Wouldn't conventional high explosives do the job as well, without any radioactive fallout?"

"Not at all. High explosives could knock out individual bombers, just pick them off. But others might get through. Most importantly, the nuclear-tipped defense missiles would not only kill several bombers at once—the weapon carriers—but they would also kill the weapons, the nuclear bombs or nuclear air-to-ground missiles that the enemy is carrying toward our targets.

"For instance, the fallout from our nuclear weapons would not endanger populations because they are smaller in yield than the big bombs or missiles designed to knock out strategic targets or even cities. Suppose we used a high-explosive weapon against an enemy bomber some fifty miles away from a big city. We would knock him out of the sky, but his nuclear bombs, if they were armed, would detonate on contact with the ground or as they were timed to go off, and the winds could carry lethal fallout to that city within a few hours. We stopped the bomber, prevented damage to the city's physical structures—and permitted lethal damage to human lives. If our interceptor pilots had used nuclear missiles against the bomber, we would have prevented both because the nuclear missiles would have destroyed its lethal payload as well as the bomber. Only minor contamination of no appreciable significance would result from the explosion of our defensive weapons and the ensuing debris of the enemy's bombs. Hundreds of thousands, perhaps more, casualties would have followed our using high-explosive missiles to kill the enemy bombers."

I might add that one of the nuclear ADC missiles—the MB-1 GENIE—could practically destroy an entire fleet of enemy bombers in a single shot, if their pilots were foolish enough to fly in even the loosest of formations.

Yet how can the Air Defense Command be *certain* that its interceptors or missiles, nuclear or conventional, perform with the deadly accuracy demanded to stop an enemy bomber fleet before it does irreparable damage to North American lives and cities? The plain answer again, as with the development of stupendous detection-alarm systems, is the ingenuity and creativity of American industry.

First, there was the creation of SAGE (Semi-Automatic Ground Environment), a continent-spanning electronic system with a high-speed digital computer as its heartbeat. Radar returns from the defense-alarm systems are digested by the computer, which compares them with the flight plans of known friendly aircraft as well as with current weather information. The system then determines the speed, altitude and direction of attacking aircraft, predicts their profile, or future course, transmits this data to the defense weapon centers and directs the interception of the enemy by defense aircraft and missiles—all within a few minutes. Automatically, the computer translates for the NORAD Battle Staff the most effective employment of these defensive weapon systems. In fact, where manned jet interceptors are concerned, directions for counterattack are fed by radio directly from the SAGE computer to the automatic pilot in the defending airplanes. Most of the SAGE sites are now being hardened against possible enemy attempts to inactivate them by long-range ballistic missile attack.

Among the radar sites that constantly feed information into the central SAGE system is one that is completely nuclear-powered. It is located at Sundance Air Force Station in Wyoming, atop a mountain peak. Because its remoteness makes the transportation of fuel oil extremely expensive, a portable nuclear power plant was airlifted to Sundance from Baltimore, Maryland, where it had been designed and built under contract with the Atomic Energy Commission by the Martin Company Nuclear Division of the Martin Marietta Corporation. A similar packaged nuclear power station also has been shipped from Baltimore to Antarctica. The stubborn imaginativeness of a leading member of American industry thus has opened bright new possibilities for the defense an progress of the Free World by making it possible to establish detection systems in out-of-the-way places as well as to reclaim for industry and commerce areas of the world formerly inaccessible for establishment of conventional power stations.

The Martin Company nuclear package supplies 1,000 kilowatts of electrical power for at least 2 years from a core of nuclear fuel that weighs 65 pounds. Heat and power for the same period from fuel oil would require well over 2 million gallons. The portable nuclear unit supplies both in enough quantity to keep a community of 2,000 persons brightly illuminated and warm. (It can become awfully dark and cold atop Warren Peak in Sundance, Wyoming.)

AUTOMATIC NUCLEAR WEATHER STATIONS

Other nuclear-power contributions by Martin Marietta to the defense of North America are automatic weather stations near both the North and the South Poles; the world's first atomic buoy, built for the Coast Guard; and a nuclear generator to power a navigational beacon on the bottom of the Atlantic Ocean. The latter obviously would tie in with current ultrasecret planning by the United States Navy for an underwater alarm system to detect hostile submarines at distances of 500 to 1,000 miles off our shores.

A most active contribution by the same Corporation's Martin-Orlando Division immeasurably aids the firepower of our aerospace defense missile batteries surrounding key American cities. This is an electronic, rather than a nuclear, system called "Missile Master."

In a sense, Missile Master separates the chaff from the wheat. By watching symbols on its electronic display console, the Tactical Director coordinates the fire of up to eight NIKE-HERCULES units. He determines if each of the units has selected the proper target. Normally, all target information goes directly to particular NIKE-HERCULES units, which then select their own targets. Since an error in target selection would be not only tragic but also dangerous to our security, Missile Master controls the situation to prevent errors. If a friendly target has been selected by mistake, or if a hostile aircraft is being ignored, or if both situations occur simultaneously, the Tactical Director can see the correct situation on a screen before him and immediately control the missile units by directing them to the hostile target or diverting them from the friendly one. There are several Tactical Directors to every Missile Master control center, each controlling eight NIKE-HERCULES units.

As General Kuter mentioned earlier, the HERCULES missile is equally effective against aircraft or airborne missiles. Either of these registers on the screens of Missile Master, which is assigned by NORAD to the United States Army Air Defense Command.

A mobile, miniaturized second-generation offshoot of Missile Master, also designed and produced for the Army at Martin-Orlando, is called "BIRDiE" for "Battery Integration and Radar Display Equipment." BIRDiE travels on wheels in a trailer 18 feet long by 7 feet wide and can be set down wherever needed to help protect civilian lives and military targets. Without excessive loss of time it can be linked up with the SAGE network or any other radar-detection and communications systems. Both BIRDiE and Missile Master can supply target information to SAGE as well as receive such information from the SAGE master-control center.

How vulnerable is the North American Continent to enemy attack? Again quoting General Robert M. Lee, former Commander of the USAF Air Defense Command: "In space defense, our position is not so good [as in air defense]."

Yes, the North American Continent may be somewhat vulnerable to an enemy attack from space—enough to cause serious worry about the future, if not the present. Yet basically we are invulnerable because of military and industrial cooperation, dedication and ingenuity. Each time an area of vulnerability is made apparent, we pitch in intensively to close off that area with technological and managerial teamwork. And such areas usually become apparent long before a potential aggressor has his firepower organized invincibly on all fronts. In this way we have always, since the end of World War II, stayed a broad-jump ahead of the enemy, despite his occasional "space-spectaculars."

Discouraging him from engaging in a surprise attack or waging massive war is a three-sided task. One vitally important aspect is almost unknown to the public and little understood by many who consider themselves expert in the concept of deterrence. It is the third keen edge of the sword of peace.

3.

The THREE-EDGED SWORD

"There is a rank due to the United States among nations which will be withheld, if not absolutely lost, by the reputation of weakness. If we desire to avoid insult, we must be able to repel it; if we desire to secure peace, it must be known that we are at all times ready for war."

—*General George Washington*

THE THIRD side to the three-edged sword of peace is superior tactical power—or the unquestionable capability to strike an enemy with certain defeat on any local battlefield of his choice. When this middle cutting edge of the sword is flanked on either side by the slashing sharpness of totally superior offensive and defensive forces, peace must be inevitably maintained. No potential enemy, regardless of his desire for conquest, would rationally attempt an attack knowing that he will be cut down swiftly on all three basic fronts of warfare. These are, of course, the strategic military and industrial complexes within his own and his allies' homelands, the tactical battlefields beyond his homeland, and the defender's homeland.

The power of the United States, if attacked, to devastate an enemy's homeland and defend the North American Continent has already been described in the two preceding chapters. But how do we stand when it comes to tactical battlefields of all kinds and sizes? What power can the Free World summon to combat a piecemeal conquest of the globe through "local" wars —the famous Communist "wars of liberation"—such as those stimulated in Korea and Laos by guerrilla tactics, such as those

73

that won a nation for the Communists in China and Cuba, and by loud boasting of strength at the international conference tables (which has gained numerous concessions for the Kremlin since the end of World War II)?

One answer to the two questions is the newly formed United States Strike Command, better known to the Military as "STRIKE." Created by decree of the Secretary of Defense on September 19, 1961, STRIKE is a unification of separate commands of the Army and Air Force. At any time, with minimum delay, STRIKE can order into battle all combat-ready units of the Tactical Air Command (TAC) and the Continental Army Command (CONARC); it also can provide the airlift to deposit troops and equipment promptly in any trouble spot of the world.

Commander-in-Chief of STRIKE is Army General Paul De-Witt Adams, a man long-experienced in guerrilla tactics and the techniques of so-called brushfire warfare. During World War II, he was a Ranger (the American counterpart of the British Commando) in the Aleutian and Italian campaigns. He was a division commander in Korea. During the summer of 1958 he led the American forces onto the shores of Lebanon after Mr. Khrushchev threatened to send Soviet tanks and other armor into that country for a Communist takeover. Mr. Khrushchev reneged on his threat after General Adams' action.

That summer I was a guest of Headquarters, United States Air Forces in Europe, at Wiesbaden, Germany. Everybody was talking about the "crisis" in Lebanon. The President of Lebanon urgently requested military aid from the United States. Shortly following the decision by the Executive Branch of our Government to grant that request, fleets of C-130 Hercules propjet transports began to land at Wiesbaden Air Base and Rhein-Main. They were carrying combat-ready troops and equipment from all over Europe as well as from the Air Force base at Newcastle, Delaware. Within 36 hours, more than 3,000 troops had reached Lebanon (an average of nearly 100 troops an hour, or nearly two every minute), including some that had arrived by sea transport.

NO WEAK POSITIONS

The new STRIKE Command can do much better than that without weakening our positions elsewhere. (For it was a fact then that the transfer of our troops from European positions left those positions open to attack. And it is a fact, well-proved by recent history, that a common Communist military approach is to pretend a strike at one point in the world to divert us while they strike in full force somewhere far removed.

With STRIKE now in existence, their problems in the achievement of such surprise moves, or even of cold-war moves, will be multiplied by many times.

General Adams lists seven superiority advantages of STRIKE in this order:

1. It provides mobile, integrated, flexible, and readily available military forces.

2. It furnishes these forces under direction of the Joint Chiefs of Staff and a single responsible commander.

3. It affords a display of force capability for cold-war operations.

4. It reduces United States reaction-time in dealing decisively and resolutely with any type of aggression.

5. It facilitates integration of CONARC and TAC operations.

6. It enhances the conduct of joint planning and joint training as directed by the Joint Chiefs of Staff.

7. It provides an organization to develop joint doctrine for the combined employment of land and tactical air forces.

General Adams concisely sums up his position with these words: "We . . . feel that the STRIKE Command will represent a potent deterrent force and will add to our military posture the kind of strength needed to give us, in the President's own words '. . . a wider choice than humiliation or all-out nuclear action.' "

The General made that statement not long after he took over the command of STRIKE. Today there would be no need for him to speak in the future tense. STRIKE *is* a going concern, "a potent deterrent force."

Yet impressive as it may be, in terms of personnel STRIKE is undoubtedly the world's smallest military command. Its total headquarters complement comprises a mere 300 officers and enlisted men, with Army and Air Force almost equally represented. Attached to that headquarters is a communications group of 311 specialists (again approximately half Army, half Air Force) that supports the mission of STRIKE. This group is the keystone of STRIKE's combat-effectiveness. It provides world-wide communications so that STRIKE Headquarters can almost instantly command fourteen tactical fighter and reconnaissance wings of TAC, the United States Air Forces in Europe and the Pacific and eight airborne armored and infantry divisions of the Army.

Neither the Tactical Air Command nor the Continental Army Command, each towering far above the STRIKE Command in personnel and equipment, can move a single unit from one position to another without first requesting approval from STRIKE. For STRIKE Headquarters has operational control, 24 hours a day, of every combat-ready unit in the TAC and CONARC. This is why a four-star general officer heads the world's "smallest" command, with the title of Commander-in-Chief.

FORMIDABLE AND VARIED WEAPONS

The weapon systems within the STRIKE domain are formidable and varied. They range through the conventional and nuclear, the supersonic and the lumbering. Included are light and heavy tanks, artillery, rifles, napalm bombs, grenades, rockets, machine guns, guided missiles, the most advanced supersonic jet fighters and slow-moving old C-47 "Gooney Birds." The extreme range is necessary if STRIKE is to perform its mission effectively. Supersonic fighters with guided missiles would be of little use in jungle guerrilla warfare, but the old C-47 could lumber in to find a clearing and drop Air Commandos or supplies, as well as drop flares to flush out the enemy. On the other hand, the

C-47 would be all but useless for close air support of ground troops on a modern battlefield. Here, the supersonic jet aircraft carrying lethal air-to-ground guided missiles are tactically required to paralyze an enemy's ground forces, inactivate his supply depots and destroy his means of logistic communications so that our own ground forces can move ahead and take over.

In order to meet and conquer all exigencies, from undeclared wars in the bush and mountains to open hostilities with modern armor, STRIKE must have at its command the most versatile arsenal of tactical weapons available. This it does have.

Since the STRIKE Command's operations are global, it must have, like SAC, a global communications system. It must also be on constant alert. In the latter respect, every member of the STRIKE Headquarters staff keeps three bags packed and stowed in the Flight Operations Building near the runway. No single staff member knows where he might have to go in a big hurry if his name is called for a particular alert, so the bags stand ready —one for the tropics, a second for the polar regions, a third for the temperate zones of the world. He has exactly 30 minutes to report for duty, regardless of the time of day or night, once his alert order is given. No more than 2 hours later, he's on his way. The purpose of the STRIKE Headquarters staff is to command the battle from an overall viewpoint by dispatching the proper divisions, wings or combat groups to a special trouble-spot— and by being on the spot with those specialized forces as needed. In some cases, the men of STRIKE, again like those of SAC, would be commanding the combat operations from an airborne command post—usually a modified KC-135 jet Stratotanker heavily laden with modern electronic communications gear. In special cases, they might even have to parachute into a region of aggression to assume command. For this eventuality they are well-equipped. The STRIKE Commander-in-Chief himself is an old-hand parachutist. The Deputy Commander-in-Chief USAF's three-star General Bruce K. Holloway, has gone through jump-training at Fort Benning, Georgia, and sports the Army Parachutist Badge on his Air Force uniform. Many other USAF members at STRIKE Headquarters have also qualified as Parachutists. Almost every one of the Army staff members wore the Parachutist Badge to begin with. The men of STRIKE are a highly skilled and specialized group.

Their job is to support a statement made by President Kennedy in his 1961 defense message: "Any potential aggressor contemplating an attack on any part of the Free World with any kind of weapons, conventional or nuclear, must know that our response will be suitable, selective, swift, and effective."

STRIKE's role normally is that of a master chess player: to shift and augment tactical air and ground forces swiftly as an occasion arises where they are needed for quenching the smoulder of aggression in any democratic area of the Earth. Yet at the same time no loopholes can be left for the enemy to weaken the total defense of our side of the chessboard.

An astute and long-experienced back-up player in STRIKE's game is the CASF, or the Composite Air Strike Force of the Tactical Air Command. Almost exactly 6 years older than STRIKE, the CASF has already twice participated in blocking armed aggressive moves by the Communists. The first instance was the earlier-mentioned Iraq-Lebanon crisis in the Middle East, where the CASF is generally credited with stabilizing the situation. The second was the Red Chinese attack at Taiwan Strait in the Pacific, to which the CASF was dispatched the following month along with additional TAC forces. CASF people did not engage in any action at Taiwan, although their very presence helped to calm the situation, proving once more that a determined show of force will cause the Communists to retreat.

In fact, Mao Tse-Tung, who led the Red Chinese guerrillas to victory against the Nationalist forces of Chiang Kai-shek, uses retreat as a basic military doctrine. In his *Collected Works*, Volume II, he stresses this doctrine as a means to exhaust an enemy. Repeatedly he states that no city or region should be held against whatever odds—unless victory is certain for the Communists. The enemies of Communism must be destroyed in parcels, he claims, by surprise attacks on small groups over which you have supreme superiority. Lead your enemy on, divide and divert him, and then annihilate him group by group. Engage only in battles that can be quickly decided in your favor, says Mao, by way of Lenin.

Obviously, Mao would have a much more difficult time of it in trying to exhaust STRIKE and the CASF than he had with the German-trained armies of Chiang Kai-shek. For both STRIKE and CASF are organized specifically to face every conceivable kind of aggression with an appropriate show of superior force. Nor can either be divided and dissected into small vulnerable portions: both are small from the start, yet each has almost limitless firepower and mobility at its command. Mao would more likely exhaust himself by pursuing his doctrine of retreat before strength.

THE SUITCASE AIR FORCE

An unwritten but ever-present motivating theme of TAC's Composite Air Strike Force is: "We keep the peace—on a moment's notice." Its members have nicknamed themselves "The Suitcase Air Force," not only because, as with STRIKE's personnel, they keep their bags packed ready to travel through any climate, but also because they are designated a full-fledged air force—and yet comprise only eighty officers and airmen plus four civilian secretaries. This small group is the entire Nineteenth Air Force, with Headquarters located at Seymour Johnson Air Force Base, near Goldsboro in eastern North Carolina. Yet "on call" to it for immediate action are seven Tactical Fighter Wings, two Troop-Carrier Wings, one Air Refueling Wing and the facilities of five Air Divisions. The suitcase-size Nineteenth Air Force answers directly and only to General Walter C. Sweeney, Jr., Commander of the entire Tactical Air Command and Commander-in-Chief of the Air Force portion of STRIKE.

The rigorous dedication of the men in the Nineteenth Air Force as well as the reason for their lightning-like response to trouble anywhere in the Free World is well illustrated by their published official requirements: "Except during authorized absences from the base, key personnel are expected to remain available to a telephone so that contact can be made *within a 2-minute period, 24 hours a day, 7 days a week.*

"Key personnel, when departing this Headquarters, will advise the Command Post in person of destination, telephone number, time en route and estimated time of return.

"In departing from quarters to duty or from duty to quarters, the Command Post will be notified of the fact prior to departure. *Eight minutes will be allowed for en route time.*

"If the individual plans to make an en route stop between quarters and duty, or duty and quarters, he will state his en route stop and the estimated time of arrival at destination to the Command Post. Upon arrival at destination he will report that the trip has been completed."

(The italics are not mine: they are a part of the official standing regulations.)

Formerly, the Nineteenth Air Force functioned as a complete unit for all exercises of the Composite Air Strike Force. These included "dry run" alerts—of which there are many, all unannounced in advance and unpredictable (since any one of them *could* be a bona fide alert), to keep the men on their toes—as well as the real thing. Recently, however, a reorganization was effected to reduce reaction time for an even swifter response to a brushfire or guerrilla outbreak. Now there are three deputy commanders for operations in the Pacific, Atlantic and Mediterranean combat areas. A fourth deputy supports and administers the CASF Headquarters.

Each combat-area deputy has a staff of experts highly specialized in the vital military aspects of his area. These include intelligence, weather, communications, politics and even economics. Daily reports in these fields are written and analyzed to keep all information fresh to the minute.

The new system permits the Composite Air Strike Force to move simultaneously in multiple directions, if necessary. If a Communist "war of liberation" flared in Iran at the same time that a brushfire war ignited in Thailand, the combat-area deputies for those regions could with ease immediately dispatch key command personnel to the trouble spot, with no interference or conflict between them. On the other hand, the CASF system is flexible enough so that personnel from all three deputates could be instantly deployed to a single trouble area, should the magnitude of the danger there warrant this.

In the event of an urgent need for large-scale deployment of CASF, due to the start, say, of a limited tactical war in Europe or Asia, the small command nucleus of the Nineteenth Air Force could be expanded explosively within a few hours by drawing on all other TAC installations to form a strike force headquarters magnitudes larger.

Regardless of the size or locale of the conflict, the CASF men operate as tactical air commanders in the field for STRIKE. They have their own aerial command posts, both jet-powered and propeller-driven. By surveying the battle area, communicating with unit commanders on the ground and squadron commanders in the air, by keeping in close touch with all the forces of STRIKE and their movements, the CASF commanders are in a position to order the astute deployment of Tactical Air Command fighter, bomber and reconnaissance aircraft so that the ground and air forces are closely integrated and the enemy is frustrated on every side.

A recent and extremely useful adjunct to CASF is COIN. It has little to do with money, except as this promotes training and equipment. COIN is a contraction of "Counterinsurgency." It completes a triumvirate of military jargon that began with "Counterforce" and "Countervalue."

Counterforce is the concept of developing and making use of a highly flexible and variegated arsenal of weapon systems, each of which is designed for the destruction of specific kinds of military targets. Its major motive is smashing an enemy to his knees through selective destruction of targets with selective weapons—without permitting a war to get out of control and involve innocent populations. In some cases, where there is unbearably intense provocation, such as might conceivably occur from the Russian side over the issue of Berlin, counterforce does not exclude the possibility of a reprisal first strike on the part of the United States. In other words, although the United States policy is committed never to start a war by attacking first, there are possible situations where a show of force might have to be physical in order to deter an enemy. For the main part, the concept of counterforce assumes that an enemy can be effectively discouraged from aggression against the Free World on a large scale if the Free World has available an arsenal of such variety and force that the enemy *knows* he will be defeated militarily no matter what his choice of weapons and targets in a surprise move may be.

Countervalue lies at the other extreme. It postulates an arsenal of restricted but overwhelmingly devastating weapons, such as intercontinental ballistic missiles with thermonuclear Re-entry Vehicles. These are planned so that they can withstand a surprise first strike by an enemy and immediately be used to retaliate on a massive scale, wiping out the enemy's populations as well as his military targets. Such a retaliation would only be placed in effect if the enemy did massive damage to our own cities and military targets. If he invaded one of our NATO Allies, for example, and took several cities, we would retaliate on the basis of the "value" of those cities and destroy the equivalent value within his own country. Some proponents of countervalue propose that the populations of target cities on both sides be warned in advance so that they may evacuate before the holocaust. This is a high-minded humanitarian viewpoint with which no normal person can disagree. But countervalue as such seems rather unrealistic (and in certain aspects rather savage), since it permits the enemy to engage in nibbling aggressions with no fear of a show of force.

The policy of the United States Department of Defense definitely favors counterforce as a means to discourage an enemy from engaging in any kind of aggression—including a massive surprise attack upon the continental United States.

TRAINING NATIVE COMBATANTS

In a special sense, counterinsurgency is but an aspect of counterforce. The COIN mission of the Air Force is to provide friendly nations with a skilled and experienced group of Air Commandos who will train the native combatants in every conceivable type of pertinent airborne operations. These include the techniques of low-level drops of paratroops, supplies and fighting equipment in the jungles; airborne marksmanship; gaining support of villagers by loudspeaker broadcasts from low, slow-moving airplanes; close air support of ground troops, day and night; reconnaissance of enemy territory; demoralizing raids and raids on supply depots; use of special air weapons to confound enemy retreats, and uncovering guerrilla movements in the darkness, to list only some of the operations. The full range extends from hand-to-hand fighting methods to psychological warfare. The idea behind COIN's First Air Commando Group is to aid the free peoples of Asia and Africa in their struggles against Communist insurrection and subjugation by providing airborne and other fighting equipment as well as special training of the natives in their use. These people of the uncommitted nations will be fighting their own wars—but at a well-equipped and skilled level that they would not normally attain. COIN techniques and tactics, with the cooperation of American industry and science, are being developed and tested for effectiveness by the First Combat Applications Group at the new Special Air Warfare Center, Eglin Air Force Base, Florida. It was at this same base that the historic Doolittle raid on Tokyo was planned and practiced during World War II. It is also here that modern manned-aircraft weapon systems are tested and improved in realistic conditions of battle.

According to the military doctrine of Mao Tse-tung, guerrilla bands must carry out their stealthy warfare in tight coordination with actions of the regular armies. With this approach, Mao conquered one of the largest nations on Earth. He accomplished this without an air force—although the Russians in

World War II proved the value of aircraft in the coordination and supply of guerrilla tactics. Mao depended entirely on radio communications to coordinate his guerrilla and army actions. With modern electronic techniques, however, conventional radio communications can be jammed or disrupted with a fair amount of ease. In fact, the Communists have made radio-jamming a special art of their own. To meet and confound this art on both the battlefield and in civilian communications, a remarkable new system has been developed (invented would be a better word) by one of the top leaders among United States defense contractors. The system is jam-proof and exceedingly mobile. It is compact, weighs only from 40 to 60 pounds per unit, and can be easily transported in jeeps, airplanes, helicopters, or be carried in a pack by our allied guerrillas. A number of the units are already in use by the United States Army and Air Force.

The new system, called RACEP, is probably the most significant development in the field of voice communications electronics since the end of World War II, which saw the invention of radar. The value of RACEP to our deterrent STRIKE posture is inestimable. It is another example of the inventiveness of American science and technology in meeting any and all threats of the Communists.

RACEP stands for "Random Access and Correlation for Extended Performance." It was conceived and developed in Florida at the Martin-Orlando Division of Martin Marietta Corporation. I spoke at considerable length with the Martin Marietta scientists and engineers reponsible for RACEP, as well as with Mr. G. T. Willey, Vice President and General Manager at Orlando. He told me: "The successful development of RACEP is unprecedented. No one ever before has devised a private telephone system without the use of wires *or* central switchboards. With RACEP, a person can 'dial' any other person and talk privately with no interference or fear that a third party may be eavesdropping."

After watching a demonstration of RACEP by Mackay Goode, Chief Engineer on the development project, I, at least, am convinced that this revolutionary system fulfills an old dream of science-fiction writers—voice-communication at will, from anywhere to anywhere else, merely by pressing a button. The prototype models developed to prove the feasibility of the system can handle 700 subscribers with each person having full use of his equipment at all times. Maximum range of the prototype units exceeds 15 miles, but the range of future production models, according to Mr. Goode, can be extended to a distance where it will be comparable with conventional voice-communications systems.

Models now being tried out by the Army and Air Force are far advanced over the original prototypes.

Because of RACEP's unique ability to use a single radio channel for multiple two-way communications without interference, a large number of stations can be operating with clear voice transmission and reception, where before only one could accomplish this feat on a single channel in the same area.

Essentially, RACEP adapts a new modulation technique enabling voices and teletype data to be carried in the form of quick pulses of radio energy on a single frequency band simultaneously between many persons and locations. In conventional radio transmissions, only one station can operate at one time on one frequency without interference. RACEP achieves its extraordinary performance by putting to use the pauses and breaks in normal conversation as well as the idle time between calls. This is done by disintegrating and coding scores of speech signals as well as teletype signals into millionth-of-a-second fragments, combining them at random and transmitting them all at one time over the same channel. Only receivers switched to the proper code for a specific conversation or message can receive it by reconstructing its fragments into a normal flow of speech or data.

Undoubtedly, one of the most urgently needed applications for RACEP is in the area of complex battlefield communications, Mr. Willey told me. "Particularly in 'brushfire' war situations will RACEP prove its value to the Free World," he said.

"But any war situation, whether static or fluid, depends for victory upon clear, reliable communications."

IMPORTANCE OF COORDINATED COMMUNICATIONS

The element of surprise is vital to paralyzing an enemy, especially in guerrilla and local war situations. Surprise attack, in turn, is largely dependent upon reconnaissance and communications. Yet once the attack has been made successfully, without dependable communications it can still fail in utter confusion. The Martin Marietta executive elaborated on this latter point. "It is no exaggeration to say that hundreds of individual radio networks, all on or near the same frequencies, are operating at the same time in the same battle zone during an average battle. Now add to this violent hodgepodge of interfering signals the other forms of radiation in that zone—radar and radio-control systems for guided missiles—and you have a situation where confusion is more normal than coordinated communications. Yet without precise coordination among all fighting, support and intelligence organizations, a military mission is more easily lost than won.

"With RACEP units mounted in trucks, tanks and the cabs of mobile missile-launchers as well as in observational aircraft and the jeeps of forward observers, clear unhampered communication may be achieved over the entire battle area with the ease of turning a knob and picking up a telephone. The Command Over-Ride code built into every RACEP receiver permits a commanding officer to 'freeze' all conversations or messages temporarily, if he has a need to announce universally important orders."

Because of the random access feature of RACEP, I might add, there is no central communications center that can be knocked out to paralyze all communications. Each RACEP unit is self-contained, a single small package, and can reach any other unit from any location, merely by turning a knob to set its transmitter to the special receiving code of the other unit.

Using RACEP, callers do not have to wait until the channel

is clear before making a call. Scores of callers on the same frequency can use that band at the same time due to the random access technique. In addition, the Command Over-Ride feature permits all receivers within range to accept an emergency call from the transmitter originating that call, regardless of whether the individual receivers are in use.

Among the several other operational advantages RACEP has over conventional communications systems are interference-rejection, commander-monitoring of every set without tuning and compact man-pack ease of transport.

The advantages of RACEP to America's tactical deterrent strength in the air, through jungles and on the conventional battlefield should be sharply evident. Many civilian fields of communications—air traffic control at busy air terminals, where nowadays the voice communication between pilots and controllers is often a "hash" of incomprehensible gibberish because of multiple interference between many transmitting stations; police and fire department networks; emergency disaster situations; ship-to-shore radio; and even private telephone-type world-wide conversations via orbital satellite relay—should also richly profit from RACEP.

The concept of RACEP was generally suggested to Martin Marietta's electronic engineers by a remarkable airborne guided missile, previously developed for the Navy at the Orlando Division. The radio-guidance system in this missile, called BULL-PUP by the Navy, also makes use (on a more elementary level) of coded electronic pulses. In the case of BULLPUP, the pulses are spurts of energy that travel invisibly through the air at the speed of light to manipulate the fins on the missile and thus direct it both horizontally and vertically straight to its target. The pilot of a tactical fighter or bomber aircraft merely watches a radar screen on his instrument panel and presses buttons on the handle of his control stick to make two blips on the screen come together. One blip is the target. The other is BULLPUP, streaking supersonically toward that target. Each time he presses a button, a coded radio signal activates a particular horizontal or vertical fin on the missile to correct its course with deadly accuracy. BULLPUP is equally effective against stationary or moving targets on the ground.

If this weapon had been available during the Korean War, the lives of many Navy fliers would have been saved. It is a standoff missile, permitting a pilot to stay out of range (as far away as 6 nautical miles) of an enemy's antiaircraft fire as he directs BULLPUP to its target.

The tragically famous problem of destroying the bridge at Toko-Ri would have been no problem for the Navy's jet airmen if they had had a weapon like this missile. The fictional bridge in James Michener's dramatic and sympathetically told novel of the same name was symbolical of thousands of real bridges that took a high toll in lives of American fliers, both Navy and Air Force. There was another situation of vital concern and danger during the Korean War that BULLPUP would have conquered with ease. It was the attempt to rout enemy trains carrying troops and supplies from the tunnels into which they speeded for protection during an aerial attack. Throughout the daylight hours, the Communist trains never left their stronghold of tunnels. They only traveled by dark, making it extremely difficult for United Nations aircraft to knock them out. Again, BULLPUP would have solved the problem: new versions of this missile are guided by radar, enabling the pilot to "see" it and its target in all lighting and weather conditions. The radar-BULLPUP is standard equipment on the Navy's newest jet attack aircraft, the Grumman A2F-1 Intruder.

BULLPUP would have saved many lives, too, by eliminating an unofficial practice of Naval aviators who attempted to flush and destroy enemy trains from their Korean tunnels. In Korea, the mountains are high and rugged and the tunnels are cut right through them. Our Navy fliers developed a technique they called "loft-bombing," which is as scary a technique as any developed in military aviation. The procedure was to fly low and fast toward a tunnel-mouth, pull up sharply releasing a bomb into the tunnel—and pray that the airplane had enough power to climb vertically on its tail so that you could safely get over the top of the mountain. The technique was not always successful. With BULLPUP, the fliers could have guided high explosives right into the mouth of the tunnels from a position in the sky miles away from the mountain faces. They could have effectively, and with almost no danger to themselves, closed both mouths of a tunnel in this way. The Korean War might have been shortenend by a considerable length of time with such a rapid foolproof method of destruction of bridges and tunnels.

BULLPUP is the only missile in the Free World—and probably in the whole world—that requires no checkout before launching. No extra support equipment is needed. It is so thoroughly reliable that once it is placed in its shipping container it demands no further attention. Months or years later it may be taken out of the container and mounted on a tactical aircraft with the complete assurance that it will work when a pilot needs it. Other missiles require periodic electronic instrument checkouts to make sure that their effectiveness has not deteriorated in storage.

VERSATILE WITH PINPOINT ACCURACY

These unhampered transport and storable qualities of BULL-PUP make it the perfect weapon for interdiction, or knock-out, raids in far-flung places of the world where climatic extremes may have adverse effects on the delicate mechanisms of missiles. BULLPUP, without suffering a reduction in efficiency, can be stored in the dank heat of jungles, aboard attack carriers in corrosive salty air, or in the stiffening cold of the Arctic regions. It is also extremely flexible, since it can be launched from supersonic jet airplanes or slow-moving helicopters. In the latter respect, the United States Marine Corps has successfully tested its versatility and pinpoint accuracy.

That same versatility and accuracy interested the Air Force, which subsequently, in cooperation with Martin Marietta engineers, developed a nuclear-tipped version of BULLPUP. The

Air Force designation for the weapon is GAM (for Guided Air Missile)-83. GAM-83A carries a conventional high-explosive warhead. The "B" Model is nuclear. From this model the Navy modified the original BULLPUP to carry a much greater high-explosive punch. Thus interservice cooperation led to an advanced form of deterrent to Communist aggression by way of "wars of liberation"—namely the brushfire and limited tactical types of war.

BULLPUP/GAM-83 arms the Navy's supersonic attack-carrier-based A4D and the Air Force's faster-than-sound F-100 Super Sabre as well as the F-105 Thunderchief, respectively a tactical fighter and fighter-bomber. But this missile can be adapted to arm almost any kind of aircraft as the need arises.

Another outstanding example of interservice cooperation to bulwark Free World security is the Navy's F4H Phantom II, a 1,600-miles-per-hour tactical fighter. Through the Department of Defense, the Air Force has purchased 336 of these outstanding airplanes during Fiscal Year 1963. Of this number, 310 are slightly modified for Air Force use and redesignated the F-110. The remaining 26 will be further modified for reconnaissance use as the RF-110. The tactical fighter versions carry the Martin-Orlando BULLPUP/GAM-83.

This airplane is as versatile as the missile. It is capable also of carrying fatal air-to-air missiles, such as the heat-seeking Philco SIDEWINDER or the Raytheon SPARROW, as well as conventional high-explosive or nuclear bombs. A comparatively small airplane in physical size, it can carry more than twice the weight in bombs than could the famous big B-17 Flying Fortress, which seemed to be the ultimate bomber at one point of World War II.

The United States STRIKE Command as well as the Tactical Air Command look forward to the F-110 and RF-110 as important modern adjuncts to their mission of discouraging aggression anywhere in the Free World.

A second-generation and even more versatile airplane is the famous controversial TFX, which stands for "Tactical Fighter/

Experimental." The Air Force operational designation for the TFX is the F-111. The concept behind this airplane transcends all controversy, a situation that was based on dollar-value versus capability of the industrial firms involved. At any rate, the contractor finally chosen was General Dynamics/Astronautics and their associate contractor was the Grumman Aircraft Engineering Corporation. But the important thing is that the TFX airplane is required to be practically all things to all men in tactical aerial warfare. It will be able to loiter slowly or reach a speed twice that of sound at altitudes that are dubbed "on the deck" by fliers. This means that it will be able to swoop over the rooftops of enemy concentration centers at a Mach 2 speed to release missiles or bombs, that it can almost float lazily over the treetops to rout guerrilla bands or otherwise engage in jungle warfare and that it can land at high speeds or low on conventional runways or on no runway at all. In fact, it is planned to be able to take off and land in very short distances on sod fields or the decks of aircraft carriers. Its versatility derives from experiments made with the X-5 Research Airplane at Edwards Air Force Base in the Mojave Desert of California during the early 1950s. The X-5 had wings with a sweepback that could be varied in flight from angles between 20° and 60°. It was designed and built by the Bell Aerospace Corporation to investigate various highspeed/lowspeed flight regimes as these were affected by an airplane's wing planform. The TFX will also have variable-sweep wings. Its ultimate value to the USAF Tactical Air Command and STRIKE should be obvious.

Supplementing and fortifying the mission of STRIKE is an awesome weapon system that is already operational. In the early fall of 1962, a unique new missile battalion started training exercises on this system at Fort Sill, Oklahoma, the United States Army's national artillery and missile training center. In a way, it was the beginning of the end to Kremlin hopes for world domination, since this missile—aptly named in honor of General John J. Pershing, invincible Commander-in-Chief of the American Expeditionary Forces during World War I—plugs the one loophole left to Communist aggression.

By the end of 1963, PERSHING Missile Battalions were ready to operate anywhere in the world, at any time, in any weather. The presence of this missile is certain to be felt at every diplomatic conference table of the future. When the representatives of uncommitted nations cast their votes, they will not be intimidated by Russian threats against them, as they so often have been in the past. They will *know* that the United States can back them up in "loophole-type" wars. The Russians also will be acutely aware of this fact.

Lt. General Dwight E. Beach, the Army's new Chief of Research and Development, put it to me this way, "A PERSHING Battalion has almost the same manned strength as a 155-millimeter howitzer battalion—with *millions* of times more firepower."

The PERSHING is strictly a nuclear weapon system. Its mission is to discourage an enemy from starting wars of the Korean type. The Kremlin has been stimulating this type, secure in the knowledge that Communist armies could get by on sheer manpower and conventional weapons during a large-scale but limited war. In this way, through the years, they have augmented their guerrilla and smaller brushfire activities. Piece by piece, they have been thus physically taking over the world. At the same time, by using threats and boasts, they have been verbally cowering the neutral nations into a cold-war fear of Communist strength. With each of their conquests, the Free World comes that much closer to enslavement.

The PERSHING Missile was developed as an instrument to preserve democratic liberties and simultaneously prevent the start of large-scale limited or general wars.

The public does not universally realize that Russia outranks the United States in terms of conventional army strength. If we were to agree that only conventional army weapons be used, there would be no stopping the Red Armies. Through massive numbers alone, they might attempt to juggernaut their way through

Europe and Asia—despite the fact that NATO's tactical air and sea power are superior to theirs.

General Agan, who was introduced in the previous chapter, once told me that "If we ever let the Communists maneuver us into a foot-soldier, rifle-shooting type of war, the battle could be lost before it began. It would be on their terms. They'd love for us to agree to this—because in this way they could whip us."

Mr. Khrushchev knows that we will not use against him the strategic types of nuclear weapons—ICBMs, POLARIS submarine-launched missiles, SAC bombers—unless he uses those types against us first. He won't do that because Communism cannot accept defeat, and defeat would be certain for the Kremlin in strategic warfare. Tactical warfare—men fighting to gain battlefield objectives—is quite another matter. Up to the time of the PERSHING Missile, Mr. Khrushchev might have been willing to risk a battle of armies. He could have, in his Communist way of thinking, balanced the number of dead soldiers against the possible gains of territory to subjugate. But now the presence of the nuclear-charged PERSHING makes this impossible. For this reason it is the final plug to stop all loopholes.

This is also why Defense Secretary McNamara has firmly stated that the United States will not hesitate to use nuclear weapons on the battlefield, if such use becomes necessary.

This attitude may seem odd in view of the recently consummated Limited Nuclear Test Ban Treaty. From all indications, the public has generally assumed that the Treaty signals an end to the threat of nuclear war, since it was ratified by the U.S. Senate on September 24, 1963 and on the following day by the USSR. In a way, the public reaction is understandable. The Treaty, except for nuclear experiments underground, not only bars testing underwater, in the atmosphere and in space but also bans nuclear explosions of any kind whatever in those media. Legally, this would include the use of nuclear weapons for warfare. Specifically, this would be to the advantage of the Soviet Union. And it is thus not too farfetched to assume that the presence of an operational PERSHING Missile was among the major military factors that convinced the Kremlin they would be gaining time to develop and stockpile their own nuclear battle-field weapons by consenting to the Treaty. They could accomplish this through massive underground testing, difficult and expensive as it might be, without violating the treaty—until they were convinced of their superiority.

The Treaty is in no way a preventative to aggression or war. Some authoritative persons, such as Dr. Edward Teller, feel that it is even an invitation to war because it retards United States' progress in new or advanced nuclear weaponry. The major purpose of our nuclear arsenal was to intimidate the Communists, to discourage them from widespread aggression. The Treaty, in some of its aspects, appears to defeat that purpose. Except that Secretary of Defense McNamara in supporting the Treaty also made it clear that the United States would in no way diminish a stand of nuclear alertness and strength.

Testifying before the Senate Foreign Relations Committee on August 13, 1963, he said: "I regard as essential to our national security the maintenance of a military posture such that we can absorb any initial surprise attack and strike back with sufficient power to destroy the aggressor."

He elaborated as follows: "In the past twenty-four months alone, there has been a one hundred per cent increase in the number of nuclear warheads in the strategic alert forces; a sixty per cent increase in the tactical nuclear forces deployed in Western Europe . . . and during the next twenty-four months it (the megatonnage of nuclear weapons) will be further increased."

If the Treaty gave any real guarantee of an end to the possibility of agression by the Communists, either through conventional or nuclear means, Secretary McNamara's action would be unnecessary. There would be no need for unquestionable nuclear superiority on our part. But the need *is* there. So long as it is, the PERSHING Missile will be a vital "plug" to enemy loopholes. For instance, our intelligence sources keep a close watch on the military maneuvers of potential enemies. The kind of buildup in conventional armor and its placement for a successful first strike against the West by the Soviet Union would take considerable time. At the first sign of suspicious mass maneuvers, we could announce withdrawal from the terms of the Treaty and retain our nuclear deterrent. The PERSHING would stand ready to discourage a tactical war.

When Khrushchev loudly denounces nuclear weapons, he does so because he knows that in these he is outranked by the United States. He is all for what he coyly calls "wars of liberation," using conventional weapons, because he is aware that in manpower alone he outranks us. It would be suicidal for him to start a nuclear war. If we had no nuclear weapons on a superior scale, there would certainly one day be a general war —started by the USSR. This is self-evident: their policy is victory for Communism by any means that will *surely* succeed.

Around the conference tables where high-placed diplomats negotiate, decisions are won on the basis of strength. With the PERSHING Missile, ultimate strength has come to the United States and our NATO, CENTO and SEATO colleagues.

EQUALLY GLAMOROUS AND VITAL

The newest big Army missile is not an ICBM that can be launched from protected underground sites to span continents, but it is equally glamorous and equally vital to the preservation of the Free World's security. For the Army, it closes a gap left by Air Force ICBMs and IRBMs as well as Navy underwater-launched POLARIS Missiles. With PERSHING, the missile-deterrent power of the United States and our allies becomes complete and awesome.

When I talked with General Beach, I asked him particularly how PERSHING fits into the global picture as an instrument to discourage war. The giant intercontinental ballistic missiles have provided a welcome stalemate, he told me, thus preventing an all-out war in the foreseeable future. "The stalemate results because the Communists know that we can absorb a surprise ICBM attack on our country and still retaliate with paralyzing power to devastate their own country's industry and ability to wage further war. So they are stimulating small-scale wars as a means to gain total victory in pieces. The PERSHING Missile will discourage this technique in many ways. It can be airlifted swiftly to any spot on Earth. Because of its extreme mobility, it is practically invulnerable. When it is deployed among our NATO friends in Europe, its presence alone will play the role of back-up to the ICBMs and medium-range strategic missiles, psychologically as well as physically."

The PERSHING Missile is described by Army officers as "the Doughboy's Sunday Punch." It can withstand the roughest conditions encountered by a foot soldier in battle. Although it can be transported with the flexibility of a band of guerrillas on the prowl, it is a big missile, a full-fledged nuclear weapon system on the grand scale—not merely an unguided artillery rocket. It was designed for rapid travel over all kinds of terrain —mountains and marshlands, forests and plains, even through the air and over water—to ambush an enemy at *his* choice of a battlefield. The roughest treatment will not diminish its lethal efficiency; it is as rugged as the much smaller BULLPUP/ GAM-83. As with the airborne missile, extremes of weather cannot bother it: it was planned in advance to operate in the sub-zero cold of the Arctic, in temperate zones, or in the steaming heat of jungles. It can be launched in a raging storm with no visibility and unerringly find a target no bigger than a baseball diamond hundreds of miles away. Its range is selective: it can be adjusted to demolish huge targets nearby or at the distance of another battlefield. The nuclear yield of its warhead is also selective: the PERSHING warhead can be preset to destroy whole supply and transportation centers, enemy military airfields, large troop concentrations, a complete enemy command headquarters, or an entire enemy armored division. It can perform these feats with a full element of surprise; no forward observers are required to sight a target and correct artillery barrages until that target is struck. The PERSHING "thinks" its own way to a chosen target with a jam-proof electronic brain. It is the ultimate weapon of the Field Artillery.

In other words, the PERSHING Missile will have the same discouraging effect upon an enemy's army commanders as the POLARIS submarine-launched nuclear missile has upon the enemy's policy planners. Like POLARIS, the PERSHING is a hide-hit-run-and-hide weapon system. It gives the United States Army and the armies of our allies tremendous nuclear firepower that is more flexible and mobile than an entire field artillery division with conventional firepower.

I saw a demonstration of the PERSHING's mobility and ease of operation in Florida at the Martin-Orlando plant of the Martin Marietta Corporation, where the missile is produced. It was the first open demonstration for the accredited press ever permitted by the Army. The PERSHING had been classified "Secret" during the 4 years of its development by Martin-Orlando, working closely with the Army Missile Command. In fact, this unique weapon system, like all other Buck Rogers-type weapons in the Free World today, was made possible only by the dedicated cooperation of free enterprise with the military.

The entire weapon system, including a complete blockhouse with an electronic computer for automatic countdown and launching, was mounted on only four tracked vehicles. These were modified from standard United States Army personnel carriers to transport the missile and its erector-launcher, a nuclear warhead, the blockhouse and a powerful jam-proof radio station for all-weather communications. They cruised at 40 miles an hour up and down gulleys, through palmetto scrub, sand and a field of pine. In 13 minutes and 55 seconds, by my watch, after they deployed for "battle," a crew of seven had attached the heavy warhead, raised the missile to launch-position, set up the radio communications system and programmed the target coordinates for the computer. The computer then took over and automatically checked out all systems in the "bird," told its self-contained "brain" where to go and launched it. The launch, in this case, was a dry run. The swiftness of the procedures, however, was standard: less than 14 minutes from deployment to launch.

"THEY WILL BE IMPRESSED"

Later, Herman Staudt, PERSHING Program Director for Martin-Orlando, gave me a graphic description of the significance of this demonstration. "When you see other tactical missile systems come over the top of a hill on their launchers," he said, "they are followed by what appears to be an almost endless caravan of vehicles transporting the required auxiliary equipment. These missiles have only half the range, or less, of PERSHING. When they're paraded through the cities and towns of Europe or Asia on show-of-force demonstration tours, the native people simply do not believe that the United States, wealthy as we are, can produce a sufficient number of them to be effective. They feel that the cost of all that equipment to support one missile would be too great for the production of more than a dozen birds. Their attitude is that the whole thing is just a propaganda show to impress them. So they're not impressed. With PERSHING, they'll see only four tracked vehicles, complete with turbine-driven power plant and air-conditioning, and they'll *know* that the cost of producing these in large quantities is not prohibitive. They will be impressed."

Impressing the uncommitted nations (as well as those already committed) is an urgently important task these days. Equally urgent is the need to keep the cost of defense production at the lowest possible level in order to maintain a balanced economy. The PERSHING, in this sense, can be called "the poor man's big missile." In terms of its capabilities, it costs less than any other modern tactical missile system. Total research and development funds invested by the Army to date amount to about 470 million dollars—a lot of money, certainly, if you're shopping for a new refrigerator, but peanuts if you're trying to buy a "big stick" to prevent war and allow your children to grow up in freedom.

The PERSHING Missile is a fine example of the competition and teamwork inherent in a free society. Fourteen contractors, including the Prime, worked as a closely knit team with six major agencies of the United States Army to design, build, test and produce successfully a precision weapon system for which there was no precedent.

A small idea of the extent of that precision was summed up concisely by Milo McCammon, General Manager of the Eclipse-Pioneer Division, the Bendix Corporation. He was talking about the self-contained guidance system in PERSHING, a system that is impervious to decoying or jamming by an enemy. He said that the system (but one of many subsystems in PERSHING) is being "mass-produced to precision standards previously attainable only in the laboratory. This required production-line manufacture of parts that are accurate to within 10 millionths of an inch. *One* millionth of an inch is equivalent to splitting the *thickness* of a dollar bill 42 thousand times."

Some concept of the incredible mobility of PERSHING was given to me by William B. Bergen, President of the Martin Company Division of the Martin Marietta Corporation, industrial manager of the entire PERSHING Program. He compared a PERSHING Battalion to a fire department. "The fire trucks," he said, "have to move—and fast—to wherever a fire erupts. They have to arrive on the scene before it's too late, with enough equipment to extinguish the blaze. Fires break out unpredictably. So do local wars. The PERSHING was designed to operate like an ultramodern fire truck—to get there with exactly the right equipment, before it's too late."

And I would like to add another tribute to the Army's most potent battlefield weapon system. I know many technical people at Cape Canaveral. All of them tell me that the PERSHING Missile has the most successful test record of any of those many marvelous systems that are developed in flight tests almost daily from the Cape. These include the giant strategic long-range ballistic missiles—ATLAS, TITAN and MINUTEMAN.

Yet the mighty, lethal, strategic backstops to America's counterforce effectiveness almost never came into being because of the caution and shortsightedness of certain very influential individuals. Only through the courage, vision and stubbornness of a scientific and military minority was it made possible for the United States to come through, meet the growing Russian ICBM threat and nullify that threat before it became a critical bargaining force of the Kremlin's.

A vital episode in American history, science and technology is the story behind our long-range strategic missile development. Without an awareness of that story, no one can fully understand the determination of the United States to block all possible roads to war and Communist conquest. It has never before been told from the inside. It began with the highest priority in our nation—a DX Priority.

4.

DX PRIORITY

"Let me say this: There has been a great deal said about a 3,000-mile high-angle rocket. In my opinion such a thing is impossible today and will be impossible for many years."

—Dr. Vannevar Bush, Chief Scientist of the United States, testifying before the Special Senate Committee on Atomic Energy, December 1945.

LATE ONE rainy afternoon in the autumn of 1944, a twin-engine transport of the United States Army Air Forces touched down at LaGuardia Field, New York. Even before it had completed its landing roll and taxied to a stop on the parking apron, a military ambulance slowly moved through the gate onto the field to meet it. Armed guards immediately surrounded both vehicles, as a tall five-star general stepped out of the airplane and walked purposefully to the ambulance, stooped over and entered.

Few, if any, of the dozen or less persons at the quiet scene could possibly conceive that they were witnessing the birth of a totally new scientific concept: aerospace power as a means to defend the Free World. In fact, almost no one then realized that a future Free World would need protection. World War II was still in progress.

Lying inside the ambulance that day was a bushy-browed old man with a leonine mane of whitening hair. He had been wakened in the predawn hours by two Army medics accompanied by military police. They had walked into his room in an upstate New York hospital and carefully but wordlessly eased him onto a stretcher. During the long drive to La Guardia Field, they could only tell him where he was going. They did not know why.

The tall general bent over him and a smile of recognition came to the old man's lips. Speaking English with a heavy accent that was predominately Hungarian but blurred through with traces of Italian, Spanish and German, he said: "Maybe you can tell me why my sleep was disturbed, yes?" The general wasted no words.

"I'm on my way back to Europe, Kármán," he said, "but as far as I'm concerned the war is over. We've broken the enemy. The rest is a mopping-up operation. It may take months and many lives will be lost. That is tragic. Yet I can't afford to be interested. My only concern is the future. I want to be sure that the military airpower of the United States is built to such a point that no aggressor will ever dare to attack us."

The old man shook his ponderous head. "For this speech you got me out of a hospital bed?!"

It was the general's turn to smile. "Kármán," he said, "you know goddamn well you can help me. Airpower is the key to strength. And science is the key to airpower. I want you to organize a committee of your most advanced scientific colleagues —to work out a concrete program for achieving my goal. I've already arranged a special office and help for you in the Pentagon."

The old man made a distasteful expression. "I refuse," he said. "I know this Pentagon. Nothing will get done. I will have too many bosses."

"You will have only *one* boss," said the general, pointing at himself. "And I should be in Europe right now. That's why I got you out of bed to meet me here. I'm in a hurry."

"With you away, it will be even worse, that Pentagon. They will strangle me in red tapes and regulations. I refuse," said the old man.

The five-star general stared straight into the old man's eyes. "Kármán," he said with conviction, "you always were the stubbornest man I know. That's one of many reasons why I want you for this mission. Nobody will block your efforts. My orders are that anything you ask for, you get without questions."

"I accept," said the old man.

Thus was born the Scientific Advisory Group of the Army Air Forces. It was later to be renamed the Scientific Advisory Board of the United States Air Force. Based on its recommendations, in less than two decades, the United States has become the greatest aerospace power on Earth.

If this little story seems almost fictional, I would like to add that it was told to me 8 years ago by the old man himself, Dr. Theodore von Kármán, one of the world's foremost aerodynamicists, as we sat in his private office in the Pentagon. The military officer was equally famous—General of the Army "Hap" Arnold. Within a year after their discussion in an ambulance, a detailed research program was presented to General Arnold in thirteen security-classified documents with the overall title of *Toward New Horizons. Science, The Key To Air Supremacy* was the introductory summarizing volume.

Through the generosity of Dr. Von Kármán, I am fortunate to have two volumes of the few original copies of those documents, now unclassified. They carefully evaluate the feasibility of supersonic aircraft, heat-seeking missiles, long-range missiles to span continents with accuracy, flight above the atmosphere and manned rocket-powered aircraft.

A typical statement from the one called *Where We Stand* follows: "Supersonic flight appeared before 1940 as a remote possibility. Supersonic motion was considered as characteristic of artillery shells; level flight supported by wings was thought to be confined to the subsonic speed range. Some people talked of the stone wall against which we were running by trying to fly faster than sound.

"One of the main results of bolder and more accurate thinking, and more experimentation in the last few years, is the fact that this stone wall disappeared, *at least in our planning, and will disappear in actual practice if efforts are continued.*" (The italics are mine.)

Early in 1944, Dr. Von Kármán and several engineering colleagues made the first engineering analysis in America of supersonic flight. It was contained in a report seen by General Arnold and was instrumental in the General's choice of Kármán as the man to organize a farsighted but practical group of scientific consultants to the Army Air Forces. At that time, a majority of aeronautical engineers, who were thinking neither boldly nor accurately, felt that supersonic flight was an impossibility. Some of the better known ones even stated this publicly.

On October 14, 1947, the so-called sound barrier was conquered in level flight by a rocket-powered airplane, the Bell XS-1, piloted by a young Air Force captain, "Chuck" Yeager. That precedent-shattering flight occurred 1 year and 10 months after *Where We Stand* was presented to General of the Army Henry Harley Arnold. Yeager is now a senior colonel, Commander of the Aerospace Test Pilots School at Edwards Air Force Base, where he made his historic flight in subsonic days. Today, hypersonic manned flight has become routine at Edwards. Hypersonic is a flight regime that starts at five times the speed of sound.

In the early documents presented as detailed reports to General Arnold by the Scientific Advisory Group is a drawing of a rocket with a range of 6,000 miles and an apogee (maximum height) of 800 miles. It is depicted on a trajectory from the West Coast of the United States to Japan. World War II, as mentioned earlier, was still in progress. But the major recommendations of the Group regarding intercontinental ballistic missiles were centered upon captured engineering studies made by the Germans for a 3,000-mile rocket. Quoting again from Kármán and his Advisory Group: "Drawings and computations had been completed for the A-10, a rocket weighing 85 tons with a thrust of 200 tons to be used as a launching rocket for the A-9, accelerating it to a speed of 3,600 feet per second. The motor of the A-9 (itself) would accelerate it further to a speed of 8,600 feet per second, giving it a range of about 3,000 miles. Some consideration was given (by the Germans) to the design of one version of the A-9 carrying a pilot. The Scientific Advisory Group agrees that the German results of wind tunnel tests, ballistic computation, and experience with the V-2 justify the conclusion that a transoceanic rocket can be developed. . . .

"The V-2 development was successful not so much because of striking scientific developments as because of an early start, military support, and a boldness of execution."

A MISSILE HORNET'S NEST

When General "Hap" Arnold read this report on the feasibility of long-range ballistic missiles, he felt that immediate action was required. As Commander of the Army Air Forces, he released a report of his own stating, in effect, that a research and development program should be supported by the United States Government to perfect an ICBM with a nuclear warhead. This report was issued to a select list of the most responsible persons in Government and the military. General Arnold, visionary and patriot, war hero and audacious man-of-action, might just as well have whacked a hornet's nest.

The man who responded most violently and negatively had himself made great contributions during World War II to both the development of the atomic bomb and microwave radar technology. He could be called the "Chief Scientist of the United States," since he was then Director of the Office of Scientific Research and Development. He was Dr. Vannevar Bush.

Nobody can question the patriotism of Dr. Bush. Only his shortsightedness can cause an eyebrow to be raised today. Then, however, he spoke with supreme authority. He was a scientist. In all sincerity he must have felt that General Arnold's proposal was a "crackpot" idea proposed by a military man stepping outside the military field. Like numerous (but not all) scientists, he must have felt at least unconsciously superior to the "military mind." At the time that he presented his caustic, derogatory opposition to General Arnold's report, he could not have evaluated the true authority of Dr. Von Kármán and others of the AAF Scientific Advisory Group—which included, to name a few, Dr. George Gamow, a physicist who had contributed much toward development of the A-bomb; Dr. Lee Du-Bridge, the present President of the California Institute of Technology; Dr. Fritz Zwicky, outstanding astrophysicist of Mount Wilson-Palomar Observatories and a world authority on jet propulsion; and Dr. Ivan A. Getting, currently Director of the Aerospace Corporation, a nonprofit scientific organization that acts as technical advisor to the Air Force Space Systems Division on advanced space projects. In fact, it is doubtful that Dr. Vannevar Bush was aware such men were behind General Arnold's report. If he *was* aware of their authority as the source of that report, his reaction against it is that much less understandable.

The report nevertheless inspired the Special Senate Committee on Atomic Energy to hold hearings in December 1945 for the purpose of determining the feasibility of an ocean-spanning rocket with a nuclear warhead. Dr. Bush's high position and reputation naturally impressed members of the Committee. He was asked to testify. Here are four brief paragraphs from his testimony that concisely (and emotionally) state his position. It was a position that, innocently, allowed the Soviets to gain a head start in developing long-range missiles from the German 200-mile-range V-2, of which they had captured about a thousand, not to mention spare parts, factories and technicians.

". . . We have plenty enough to think about that is very definite and very realistic," Dr. Bush told the Senators, "— enough so that we don't need to step out into some of these borderlines which seem to be, to me, more or less fantastic.

"Let me say this: There has been a great deal said about a 3,000-mile high-angle rocket. In my opinion such a thing is impossible today and will be impossible for many years.

"The people who have been writing these things that annoy me . . . have been talking about a 3,000-mile high-angle rocket, shot from one continent to another, carrying an atomic bomb and so directed as to be a precise weapon which would land exactly on a certain target, such as a city.

"I say, technically, I don't think anybody in the world knows how to do such a thing, and I feel confident it will not be done for a very long period of time to come . . . I think we can leave that out of our thinking. I wish the American public would leave that out of their thinking."

Because of Dr. Bush's vehement attitude, the first fully successful test flight of an ICBM was not to occur for an even dozen years. It was the ATLAS 12A, launched from Cape Canaveral on December 17, 1957. There had been two previous launches of ATLAS from the Cape that same year, on June 11 and September 25, but these were only partially successful. Stubbornly, General Arnold had fought for a budget and funded a modest research program on ICBM technology during 1946 and 1947. This was the highly secret MX-774 Program, contracted in April 1946 with Consolidated-Vultee, now the Convair Division of General Dynamics Corporation. By the end of June 1947, the program was canceled: the Army Air Forces missile budget had been cut to less than half, from $29,000,000 to $13,000,000, for Fiscal Year 1947, due to Congressional reduction of the total AAF budget. The next 7 years were an arid wasteland through which no Government funds were available for research and development of an ICBM system.

NO HOWLING SUCCESSES

When the MX-774 Program was canceled, a test missile had not yet been launched. A small portion only of the budgeted $1,893,000 had been consumed in engineering studies. Consolidated-Vultee appealed to the Army Air Forces for permission to use the remainder of the budget, since it was already on the books, to build and flight-test three missiles. The AAF agreed. Three MX-774s were launched from the Army's White Sands Proving Ground, New Mexico, during 1948. They were not howling successes, but valuable data were gathered from the flights. These data eventually were used as a basis for the design of the ATLAS long-range missile. It is interesting to note that the rocket engine used in the MX-774 was exactly the same as that used in the Bell XS-1 by "Chuck" Yeager when he made the first manned flight through the sound barrier. It was a four-barreled engine that developed 6,000 pounds of thrust (8,000 pounds thrust, in the case of MX-774, which carried more fuel) and could be lifted and moved about with ease by two men.

Along with the MX-774, ten other missile projects were canceled by the AAF because of budget reduction or unresolved technical problems, or both. Altogether, there had been 27 missile projects in the works. The long-range intercontinental type of surface-to-surface missile had the lowest priority then. There were too many objections against its feasibility, even among some quarters in the AAF. The two main objections were that it was improbable, if not impossible, that a guidance system could be developed with sufficient accuracy to keep a missile on course for thousands of miles and that a nuclear warhead could ever be reduced enough in size and weight to make it transportable by missile. Dr. Vannevar Bush, of course, spearheaded the opposition to those who claimed that these two objections could be overcome.

Lieutenant General Donald L. Putt, who retired from the Air Force as Deputy Chief of Staff for Research and Technology, made a cogent observation about the situation in early 1952. The new United States Air Force, a separate military department, was then less than 5 years old. Its Air Research and Development Command had been established 2 years and a month earlier, just 8 days after the death of General of the Air Force Henry "Hap" Arnold on January 15, 1950. This Command was destined to carry forth the visionary tradition of General Arnold. That destiny was aptly forecast by General Putt, writing in the February 1952 issue of *Air Force* magazine.

"I feel," wrote the General, "that Dr. Bush undoubtedly would have spoken differently had he either participated in an intensive study of airpower research and development problems, or had he been in General Arnold's position at the time. Needless to say, the Air Force has been and will continue supporting a program for developing intercontinental missiles. And substantial progress is being made toward our ultimate goal—the development of an intercontinental guided missile of supersonic speed and equipped with an atomic warhead.

"My reason for being explicit about this is to emphasize the point that each individual must look beyond what he reads about guided missiles. The only sound way to eliminate confusion and evaluate a man's statements in this field is to learn first about his background—his training, experiences and prejudices —and then to evaluate his statements accordingly."

General Putt was not referring to the ballistic type of long-range missile, which even in 1952 was considered by most scientists to be a dream stimulated by Buck Rogers. His reference was to a winged cruise missile, a pilotless bomber guided through the atmosphere by electronic or optical systems that used the stars as navigational reference points. Such a missile would require hours rather than minutes to reach targets a continent away, since it would be propelled by conventional turbojet engines rather than by a rocket engine. Its speed could reach perhaps three times that of sound. An intercontinental *ballistic* missile, on the other hand, is like a huge bullet without wings. For the greater portion of its journey, it travels outside the atmosphere. Using rocket power, it is boosted to speeds in excess of Mach 20 (twenty times the speed of sound) and can strike at targets halfway across the world within 30 minutes after launching. In 1952, the slow intercontinental cruise missile appeared to be the most practical approach to automatic transoceanic weapons. But the ICBM was not forgotten, despite its disrepute.

Certain scientists and military officers of the Air Research and Development Command, as well as those of what now is the Air Force Scientific Advisory Board, knew that an ICBM was not only possible to achieve but that an immediate start of developmental work was required. Intelligence information from beyond the Iron Curtain had already indicated this a half-dozen years earlier.

SOVIET ICBM PLANS

Regarding such information, I spoke with Frank A. Burnham, Chief of Plans and Programs for the Office of Information, Air Force Space Systems Division. To quote him verbatim: "In the immediate post-World War II period—1946, early '47, to be exact—this country obviously had an intelligence capability equal to that of the Soviet. We had a pretty good idea of what the Soviet was planning to do—and was, in fact, then implementing in terms of the development of long-range ballistic missiles of the ICBM type. With the success of Soviet intelligence and espionage in getting our atomic bomb—our first crude and rather large unwieldy atomic device—we were then quite sure that they were going ahead with the urgent development of a huge ICBM rocket booster. A booster with sufficient thrust to make it capable of hurling this first relatively crude atomic device across intercontinental distances."

I interrupted Mr. Burnham. "Were you *assuming* this, or was there concrete intelligence information?"

"Well, there was some pretty concrete information," he answered emphatically. "The how and the wherefore of that information is the how and the wherefore of most of our intelligence information—and this must remain classified. But it was pretty concrete—to the effect that *this* was what the Soviet *was* going to do. The Soviet had inherited more hardware and perhaps more of the mechanical ability of the German V-2 Program than we had. We inherited many of the scientific brains and geniuses instead. But the Soviet had the practical wherewithal to start tinkering on a large scale."

Despite the intelligence knowledge and evaluation of Soviet plans, our own ICBM program lagged deep into 1953. The reasons now were various. Economics came on stage. Those who were convinced that an ICBM could be developed were awed by its probable cost in dollars. They were thinking in terms of a gigantic rocket with tremendous thrust that would be needed to carry the ultraheavy nuclear warheads then available. They refused to concede that smaller warheads with the same yield were possible of attainment. In a free economy, they reasoned, it would be fatal to concentrate most of your resources in a single project. Other military development programs were more urgently needed to deter an enemy from aggression. Jet fighters and bombers, for instance, required development, as did air-to-air, air-to-ground and ground-to-air combat missiles. A modern Air Force had to have a variety of modern weapons for strength and flexibility. All these development programs were exceedingly expensive but worthy of a budget because they were practical. The completely unknown quantity that was the ICBM could serve only to decelerate these vital immediate programs if dollars were diverted from them to a grand-scale additional program, the immediate results of which were not apparent.

A year earlier, however, in January 1951, a small budget was approved by the Air Force to establish Project MX-1593. Its purpose was to study the relative merits of rocket-powered versus glide missiles. The glide missile, much cheaper to develop, could be launched into enemy territory with a heavy nuclear warhead from a high-flying jet bomber. This study showed that a rocket-powered ballistic missile had many advantages over the glide missile. So a code name was assigned to further study on the ICBM. It was Project ATLAS.

Consolidated-Vultee, which had continued ICBM studies on a modest company budget after Project MX-774 funds were depleted, had meanwhile been given an Air Force contract to elaborate on those studies. Things may have seemed to be looking brighter. They were not. Another strongly influential opponent to the ICBM had come on the scene in early 1953. He was Charles E. Wilson, appointed Secretary of Defense by President Eisenhower. In fact, Secretary Wilson was somewhat upset to find so many different shorter range missile programs being pursued simultaneously by the three military departments. He felt that there was needless duplication and ordered a stringent evaluation of these programs. His idea was to cut down on some and speed up others.

The Scientific Advisory Board of the Air Force had previously inaugurated an *ad hoc* committee for Project ATLAS. It was headed by Dr. Clark B. Millikan of CalTech. This committee reviewed all available ICBM data and recommended to the Secretary of the Air Force that a step-by-step program be followed, using existing rockets where possible, to solve the thorny key ICBM problems of accurate guidance over intercontinental distances, re-entry heating of the warhead by friction with the atmosphere and propulsion systems of sufficient stability and thrust to propel a big missile and its heavy warhead above the atmosphere, onto a selected trajectory.

Another important move of the Scientific Advisory Board was the establishment of a Nuclear Weapons Panel. For even if all of the foregoing problems could be solved, there still remained the ultimate solution: development of a nuclear warhead with an economically and militarily acceptable weight-to-yield ratio. The panel, mainly composed of outstanding nuclear physicists, was to consult on the feasibility of nuclear warheads for ICBMs, in addition to other kinds of nuclear weapons. One of its members was Dr. Edward Teller, now generally known as "Father of the H-bomb."

FUTURE NUCLEAR WARHEADS

Chairman of the panel was John von Neumann, a short, balding, kindly appearing man with thick dark eyebrows. At the time he had just turned 50. His modest and friendly appearance belied the strength of his will and intellect, for if any single man can be given the credit for breaking the ICBM deadlock it was Dr. "Johnny" von Neumann. Not only was he a brilliant mathematical physicist, but he was also a warmly human person. He inspired great respect with both aptitudes. He was probably the only scientist in the United States who could get the controversial Project ATLAS into full swing on the basis of a warhead that did not yet exist. The design requirements of America's first ICBM were conceived on just that basis. Such was the confidence stimulated in other scientists by Dr. von

Neumann. But let a close associate of his describe the situation.

Colonel Benjamin Paul Blasingame was in the thickest part of the ICBM struggle and made vital positive contributions to it. When I talked with him not long ago at the AC Sparkplug Division of General Motors in Milwaukee, Wisconsin, the legend on his office door read: "Dr. B. P. Blasingame, Director of Engineering." Tall and ruggedly handsome, Blasingame spent the maturing years of his youth in the Pentagon as Project Officer in the Office of the Air Force Assistant for Development Planning. The conflict over the ICBM centered in that office. He was 32 years old when he entered its doorway, 36 when he left to participate in one of the most astounding success stories in the history of technology. His Pentagon tenure spanned the 4 most fateful years of America's ICBM program—from the fall of 1950 to the summer of 1954. Just prior to his Pentagon job, he had received his doctorate in Aeronautical Engineering at the Massachusetts Institute of Technology, where he had worked closely with Dr. Charles S. Draper, famed Chairman of MIT's Department of Astronautical and Aeronautical Engineering. Together they had worked on private research projects in the field of inertial navigation devices. Dr. Blasingame thus became a specialist in a type of guidance system that many engineers felt was as impossible of achievement for long-range accuracy as the ICBM which required it.

Of the incredible mathematical insight that made an American ICBM possible, Dr. Blasingame had this to say: "Johnny von Neumann had been very intimately associated with the whole A-bomb and H-bomb development programs in this country. Not only did he know precisely what was available today, but he was sufficiently discerning to *know* what was going to be available tomorrow. So John's *very, very* important input to us in Air Force planning was to *specify* during the very early stages of our ICBM proposals what the weights and approximate sizes of nuclear warheads would be in the future. We based our planning on his certainty that a small high-yield thermonuclear warhead was practical and achievable. This later was worked out in more detail with the Atomic Energy Commission. But the point I'm trying to make is that without von Neumann's predictions about how these warheads could be developed, the ICBM program never would have succeeded.

"The group that develops nuclear weapons is characteristically very conservative. Many such developments foundered because the warhead specifications were proposed in terms of enormous sizes and enormous weights that made the whole weapon system impractical. Von Neumann's personal influence in our case permitted the ICBM program to be based upon a *projected* warhead, rather than one derived from the then current technology."

At one point in the contest, Dr. Blasingame was summoned by the Nuclear Weapons Panel of the Air Force Scientific Advisory Board and asked to present detailed forecasts on the development of nuclear warheads for ICBMs. His task was to give reasonable proof that by the time an ICBM was developed into functional hardware, there would be an adequate warhead ready for it. "Of course, I'm not a physicist," Blasingame told me. "At the most, I would call myself an engineer. So I suspect that I knew very little of the physical basis for the predictions I had. These I had gathered with the help of von Neumann. The men I faced, including Johnny, were all great scientists in the field of physics. And when I showed them these predictions—and they were predictions on which we wanted to base actual missile designs—their reaction was: 'Where in the world could you ever get predictions such as these?! Obviously they are totally inaccurate!' Without hesitation, von Neumann stepped up and said, 'Yes, perhaps. But I suspect they are a whole lot more accurate than any predictions this Panel can give him!' Well, it took only a few years after that to demonstrate the fact that von Neumann knew what he was talking about. They did turn out to be accurate projections."

John von Neumann was one of a group of five Hungarian-born scientists who chose the United States as their permanent homeland prior to the outbreak of World War II. All unstintingly gave their genius to the defense of democracy. The patri-arch among them was Theodore von Kármán, who until his death at the age of 81 on May 6, 1963, continued to advise the Air Force on important matters and directed scientific re-search and development programs for the North Atlantic Treaty Organization. Among them also are Edward Teller, Leo Szilard and Eugene Wigner—all nuclear physicists who have made profound contributions to the control of atomic energy for peaceful uses as well as for deterrent weapon systems. In his book, *The Legacy of Hiroshima*,* Dr. Teller characterizes von Neumann as the man "who pioneered the development of computers [and] was said to be the only human with a mind faster than an electronic brain."

Tragically and ironically, on February 8, 1957, John von Neu-mann died from incurable cancer, before the first perfected ICBMs were deployed in operational sites with their nuclear Re-entry Vehicles attached. He was only 54 years old. But he did live to see the mightiest deterrent to war on Earth become an official fact because of his efforts. He continued even there-after to provide potent suggestions and lead the way toward a higher degree of security for the United States. Dr. John von Neumann resisted leaving anything to chance in the lifeblood struggle with communism.

AWARENESS OF KREMLIN BLACKMAIL

If the Russian Communists had achieved operational ICBMs and the United States had none, there would have been no ICBM counterforce in the Free World. The Kremlin would have been in a supreme position to impose missile-power black-mail on all nations with ease. Johnny von Neumann was always acutely aware of this.

So were a few others. Among them was a certain young Air Force colonel working in the Pentagon along with the then Colonel Blasingame. This young officer, Bernard A. Schriever,

* Edward Teller and Allen Brown, *Legacy of Hiroshima* (New York: Double-day & Company, Inc., 1962).

was so disturbed by the lack of a coherent program to develop actual ICBM hardware that he continually urged von Neumann and anybody else he could find with the proper experience or capability to suggest practical ways for the reduction of weights and costs per yield in nuclear warheads. Schriever was, of course, a member of the unfashionable pro-ICBM minority in the Air Force—a minority that was nevertheless larger than its equivalent group of supporters in the Executive Branch of the Government. All of them waited anxiously for results of the thermonuclear tests at Bikini Atoll in the Pacific during the months of March to May 1953. The public hadn't the faintest concept of the significance of those tests, which were designated "Operation Castle." Even after the tests were completed, the results were obscured by secrecy.

The secrecy was not softened despite a shattering announcement by the Kremlin 3 months after Operation Castle was concluded. The new Soviet Premier at that time, Georgi Malenkov, boasted to the world in August 1953 that Russian scientists had exploded an H-bomb with huge success. The United States, if this were true, was no longer the sole possessor of unimaginably devastating thermonuclear weapons. There was no way for our scientists to determine the exact weight and size of the Russian H-device, but its yield could be calculated. This was enough to shake some influential people out of their ICBM lethargy. For the Soviet controlled economy *could* be concentrated on the development of an ultra-expensive giant carrier rocket to transport the H-bomb, regardless of its size and weight. The Russians still had to solve the vital problems of re-entry heating and guidance across continents, but in the latter technology they might not feel that tightly accurate target requirements were necessary. They might, in fact, plan on developing a terror weapon that was merely required to hit within a nation or a large city, much as the V-2 had been used by the Germans. The V-2 had carried a conventional high-explosive warhead—and it had been terrifying enough. A single shot carrying a high-yield thermonuclear warhead, if successful, might conceivably demoralize an entire population. So reasoned many of our military and diplomatic planners. At that time there was no detection-alarm system to warn a continent of the approach of missiles. And ballistic missiles, once they are on course after engine burn-out, are silent. Their approach could be a complete surprise, since visually they are almost impossible to detect if they are launched secretly.

A sense of real urgency now moved every champion of an American ICBM program. Additional champions came on the scene. The stage was brilliantly lighted in October 1953, when Dr. John von Neumann circulated a simple statement to all concerned. The statement was based on a final evaluation of the results of the Operation Castle tests. It was no longer a forecast based on mathematical calculations. By then Johnny von Neumann was Chairman of the Air Force Scientific Advisory Board. His statement was rigorously official. It represented the concurrence of all board members.

It said: "Thermonuclear weapons of small weights and sizes *can* be produced."

One month later, a Strategic Missiles Evaluation Committee was set up by Trevor Gardner, then Assistant to the Secretary of the Air Force for Research and Development. Gardner had been among the ICBM champions almost from the time he was appointed by Air Secretary Harold Talbott. The Committee resulted from the previously mentioned demands of Defense Secretary Wilson that all missile programs or plans be given a long hard look by each military department.

Within a year, the Air Research and Development Command of USAF was given a DX Priority to proceed at full throttle on Project ATLAS. This is the highest priority of the United States. The "D" stands for "Defense" and the "X" symbolizes "supreme urgency."

WEAPON SYSTEM-107A

Less than 30 days after the Project was lifted to DX status, a dozen Air Force officers and scientists were presented with

Top Secret Travel Orders. Their destination was an abandoned parochial schoolhouse in Inglewood, California, a suburb of Los Angeles. They were required to travel across the continent singly and to wear civilian clothes at all times. At the beginning of Fiscal Year 1954, on July 1st, they met in the schoolhouse to establish the Western Development Division of the Air Research and Development Command. Among them were Paul Blasingame and Bernard Schriever. The latter's uniforms, locked in a closet back East, now sported a shiny new star on each shoulder tab. Schriever had been promoted to the rank of Brigadier General in keeping with authority he would assume in his role of Commanding Officer of the embryonic Division. Under him at the time was a military team of five hand-picked officers, each a scientific or engineering specialist, and six Air Force civilian scientists. The official designation of their program was WS (for Weapon System)-107A. The very designation was classified Top Secret, as was the more popular name, Project ATLAS.

General Schriever, who before he left the Pentagon had headed the Air Force Office of Development Planning, was in an excellent position to evaluate the aptitudes and qualifications of the men he chose to work with him in California. His choices were made not only on the basis of their military backgrounds but, more importantly for a project of this magnitude, on their scientific, engineering and managerial talents. No one with less than a Master's degree in science or engineering was chosen. The Strategic Missiles Evaluation Committee, also chaired by Dr. von Neumann, had not merely evaluated the feasibility of the giant WS-107A Program but had actually worked out its guidelines and made a series of recommendations to the Secretary of the Air Force regarding *how* such an unprecedented program *could* be successfully accomplished. The keynote was "management." The military officers involved were to perform the role of scientific and engineering executives, supported by an extremely capable civilian group.

An outstanding executive, whether civilian or military, must have three inbred qualities: the courage to make decisions, the personality and knowledge of his subject to inspire confidence and the insight as well as the ability to delegate full authority to the proper persons under him.

As top military executive, General Schriever's first big delegation of authority was to appoint the Ramo-Woolridge Corporation as technical director of Project ATLAS. The Corporation was also to provide systems engineering. Drs. Simon Ramo and Dean Woolridge, two forward-looking young scientists, had formed the Corporation and had been carrying forth long-range analytical studies for the Air Force on the original foundation constructed by Dr. Theodore von Kármán at the behest of General of the Air Force "Hap" Arnold. Now, in October 1954, Ramo and Woolridge were assigned the task of managing the almost insurmountable problems involved with America's first tremendous leap into military space-weapon systems. That was four months after the Western Development Division was established. Two months later a basic decision had been made on the configuration of the ATLAS ICBM.

"Configuration" is a misleading word here. Not only applicable to the external shape of the missile, it is a broad outline of the total weapon system. This includes all subsystems—mechanical, electronic and human—as well as the "bird" itself. It concerns Ground Support and Ground Operational Equipment (respectively abbreviated by missilemen as GSE/GOE), logistic support and personnel concepts, which encompass the training of combat missile crews, among other things.

The decision on the ATLAS configuration could only be made by General Schriever, whose Division had complete authority and control over all aspects of the development program for WS-107A. By April 1955, the official development plan was published by the Western Development Division and circulated among defense contractors with the experience and security clearances to receive it. The plan called for the first launch-capability from an *operational* base no later than July 1959. This must have seemed like an impossible requirement to many contractors, all of whom were accustomed to lead times of from 12 to 15 years in the development of new weapons. This plan reduced by two-thirds the development time for a weapon system in which nobody had any real technological experience. Yet mid-1959 was an operational requirement, if the United States was to meet the Russian ICBM threat in time to countermand it.

Actually, the first operational ATLAS was successfully launched from Vandenberg Air Force Base on September 9, 1959—two months and a week late. It was roughly equivalent to planning the perfection of an automobile on a quarter-century schedule—and producing the first successful model a day late. In the case of WS-107A, the tribute to superb management, supreme technical accomplishment and exceptional doggedness of purpose must be more or less equally divided among the men of General Schriever's Division, those of the Ramo-Woolridge Corporation, North American Aviation's Rocketdyne Division, General Electric and those of Convair, the major contractor on ATLAS from June 1955 when that concern was selected as the industrial manager of the program on the validity of its competitively submitted engineering proposal for the job.

THE FREE WORLD'S MIGHTIEST MISSILE

But already, a month earlier, in May, Schriever's Division had been authorized by the Air Force to proceed with Project XSM-68, an alternate ICBM configuration. The "XSM" stood for "Experimental Strategic Missile." Today, it is known as TITAN, the mightiest ICBM in the Free World's arsenal. As General Schriever once told me: "I don't think that anyone of the American public is aware of SM-68. Yet it's the real designation for TITAN."

The General also told me why there was a deep need for SM-68: "Professor John von Neumann, and the scientists under him, who recommended an accelerated ICBM Program felt *very, very* strongly that there should be an alternate technical approach. You have to place yourself back in that period, 1954 and 1955, when a lot of people didn't think that the ICBM was even possible. There were *many, many* technical doubts about it. So the von Neumann Committee felt strongly that we should have an alternate approach, just as in the atomic bomb project where you had the implosion approach and the gun approach. In other words, there were two technical approaches. They were not duplicating their efforts in any sense of the word on the Manhattan Project. In the ICBM program we had the stage-and-a-half, the balloon tank structure of ATLAS—there were many questions about this—and the full two-stage system of TITAN. So these were very definitely different approaches at the technical level. Again, there was no duplication in *any* sense of that word."

Briefly, the "balloon tank structure" mentioned by General Schriever refers to an ingenious concept developed by Karel J. Bossart, an aeronautical engineer at Convair, during the MX-774 experiments. In actuality, the MX-774 test-missile was a stripped-down version of the German V-2. Bossart, who was prime mover on this early Convair (Consolidated-Vultee) program as well as on the later ATLAS Project, hit upon the idea of saving weight by removal of all internal supports for the missile airframe. By pressuring the metal skin of the missile with an inert gas, much as a toy balloon is pressurized and holds its inflated shape with air, an extremely thin metal could be used for the skin without a need for other kinds of support. When fuel and liquid oxidizer were pumped into this balloon-like missile, most of the pressurizing gas was displaced and escaped through a valve. The fuel and oxidizer almost completely supported the missile's shape. It was, in effect, one big fuel tank with the fuel separated from its oxidizer by a single, simple bulkhead. The later ATLAS, many times larger than MX-774, was based on the same concept. A tougher, sturdier metal alloy skin was employed, but the Air Force was bothered by the possible problems that could develop. Nevertheless, the concept at that time appeared to be the best way to get an ICBM off the launch pad in the shortest possible time.

General Schriever also mentioned the "stage-and-a-half" configuration of ATLAS. To elaborate: the ATLAS had three main rocket engines. Two of these were mounted on a collar that dropped away from the missile at altitude. These were the booster engines that helped to propel ATLAS up through the stratosphere, whence it continued onward with a single engine. All three engines were ignited on the ground, thereby sacrificing a certain amount of efficiency in power. The twin-engined collar was not exactly a booster stage in terms of today's definition of a stage, so it has been generally considered a half-stage.

The ATLAS has turned in an amazing performance for its limitations. It is a lethal, highly accurate, highly potent long-range deterrent weapon system today in SAC's arsenal. My purpose in describing those limitations was to elaborate for the reader upon the complex technical difficulties that faced the Air Force's Western Development Division—popularly referred to as "WDD"—at a time when the state of the art in long-range ballistic missilery was virtually nonexistent. The stainless steel "balloon" that was ATLAS could be considered only as one approach—if our nation was to survive.

The alternate approach was a full two-stage missile, or at least a missile that would ignite its final stage beyond the thick air-drag of the lower atmosphere. When these requirements were circulated to a carefully chosen list of contractors, there were almost as many engineering approaches to WDD's requirements as there were contractors. For example, Lockheed proposed an ICBM with two huge boosters "strapped" to its sides. These would carry the missile up to where the air was thin and the drag against flight practically nonexistent, then they would automatically drop away as the missile's engine ignited. The idea had fine possibilities, although Lockheed was not awarded the contract. The same concept is being used today for TITAN III, with an essential difference. The strap-on boosters are solid-fuel rockets, which are less complicated and much more reliable for this particular kind of operation. In those days, fueling operations alone would have added problems with the Lockheed concept, which employed what amounted to three huge liquid-fuel rockets, each with its own tanks and fuel load. The three engines of ATLAS are fed from the same tanks.

AN AWESOME RESPONSIBILITY

The contract for WS-107A-2 was finally awarded to The Martin Company, now called Martin Company Division of the Martin Marietta Corporation. Chosen as Prime Associate Contractor (in other words, the industrial systems manager), Martin became responsible for fabricating the ICBM airframe and integrating the work of other associate contractors (guidance and propulsion) as well as all subcontractors. The company also had full responsibility for testing the missile in both simulated and actual flight conditions. It was an awesome responsibility. The SM-68 ICBM proposed by Martin Company engineers had two full stages. One was ignited on the ground; the other in space. Both stages were to be fabricated from a copper-aluminum alloy with walls the thickness of a half dollar. The walls were to be heavily reinforced internally with extruded ribs. SM-68 was proposed as a rugged "blockbuster" of a long-range missile. It seemed almost impossible of achievement at that stage of missile technology. Yet the Air Force was convinced that it could be made to work.

No weapon-systems contractor is chosen by pulling numbers out of a hat. By the time the Martin Company was chosen for SM-68, Source Selection Boards had been established at the Western Development Division for the selection of contractors to develop ICBM hardware. Painstakingly, the original half-dozen officers that had founded WDD expanded their ranks. They did this scientifically by setting up rigid requirements and programming these into an IBM sorting machine. Included in the requirements was a university degree in engineering or science. Then they requested that personnel punch-cards from

Air Research and Development Command Headquarters be run through the machine. When the SM-68 contract was awarded, WDD personnel numbered 270 highly motivated officers. Four years later, when the first SM-68 TITAN was successfully launched from Cape Canaveral, there were 4,760 people working at WDD (already renamed the Ballistic Missile Division). Less than 21 per cent of this population held no college degree; this group was composed mainly of supporting personnel, such as secretaries, librarians, clerks and security-guards. Approximately 80 per cent of the Division officers held Bachelor of Science, Master of Science and Doctor of Philosophy degrees, whereas the entire Air Force average was 50 per cent.

Men of this calibre served on the Air Frame Source Selection Boards in the early days. These Boards' standards of intelligence, outstanding achievement in engineering or science and dedication to the cause of democracy have not diminished today. The one concerned with the selection of a contractor for an alternate ICBM was no exception.

Dr. Alfred Rockefeller, Jr., then official historian of the Division, concisely described to me how that Board evaluated the contractor proposals for SM-68 TITAN. "First of all," he said, "the Board is made up of Air Force officers here plus technical advisors from other parts of the Air Force—research and development people, materiel people and civilian technical advisors for back-up on specific questions. The civilians are from our nonprofit systems engineering and planning organization. The names of these men are held in the strictest secrecy, as is the location where they study the contractor proposals. The purpose is so that they cannot be influenced in any way in making their decisions. However, I can give you the name of the man who headed the particular Board that decided on the TITAN. He is now a major general, Charles H. Terhune, Jr., one of the real ICBM pioneers. He ran the Board. He's now Commander of the Air Force Systems Command's Electronic Systems Division in Massachusetts. I can tell you a story about that source selection, because I was around at the time.

CHOSEN ON PAST ACCOMPLISHMENTS

"Contractors are invited to a prepoposal briefing on all new projects. They are chosen on their past accomplishments, the quality of their scientific, engineering and technical staffs, their work facilities and other resources. They are told what the requirements are for the project and sent home to work out proposals on their own in a specified period of time. They get no further help from the Air Force until they come back with their proposal. The proposals finally submitted by the contractors are then studied on the basis of their own validity, against which is compared the rigorous criteria of staff quality, past accomplishments, work facilities and so forth. In this case, there were some outstanding companies competing—Douglas, Martin, Lockheed and others. The Board's selection session took 30 days. Some of the people on the Board complained because Terry, General Terhune, got them in the conference room at 7 o'clock in the morning and refused to let them leave until 10 o'clock at night—every morning and every night. I mean *seven* days a week for a month."

The foregoing anecdote should provide the reader with at least a faint idea of the sense of urgency that pervaded the Western Development Division. Back in Washington, the Strategic Missiles Evaluation Committee not only recommended the programs for WDD, but also set up the target-dates for their completion. The grueling compression of time demanded by the Committee required an actually superhuman effort on the part of the Division. Its members, having sole authority over the ICBM programs, were in a real sense guardians of the near-future security of the United States. If they failed to meet the imposed "impossible" deadlines, they were failing 180,000,000 Americans. I know many of these men. I can vouch for a fact that this was exactly the way they felt.

Yet the task before them should have discouraged any normal human being. Not only were they faced with a long-range ballistic missile test program, but they had to see that the tests were made possible after the missiles were built. Simultaneously, they were involved with hundreds of programs, all of which converged in the completed missile. The Atlantic Missile Range had to be organized and extended thousands of miles through the South Atlantic Ocean. Tracking and recording instruments had to be designed, built and installed on Cape Canaveral, on islands through the range and in ships and aircraft. The Pacific Missile Range had to be established with cooperation of the Navy. Data-processing techniques had to be developed to analyze the instrument recordings. Re-entry Vehicles had to be designed, built and tested under ICBM conditions—before the ICBMs themselves were available. Training manuals for combat missile crews had to be similarly written. The only logical approach was to assign these multifarious subprojects to civilian contractors with a foundation of experience in the required engineering or scientific fields. The major systems contractors, of course, managed their own data analysis and testing of components. But men of the WDD and Ramo-Wooldridge had to keep up with the overall technology and tie loose ends together in addition to working closely with the contractors. The stupendous time compression and almost overwhelming technical management problems inherent in the ICBM development programs inspired the inauguration of a new military approach to research and development of weapons. It was the concept of "concurrency."

The best definition of this word that I have encountered was given to me by Major General Osmond J. Ritland, who was Commander of the Ballistic Missile Division (née WDD) during one of its most critical periods. "By its very name," says General Ritland, "concurrency requires simultaneous action across different areas and at varying levels. It demands a vast and *continuous* interplay of objectives and achievements, all geared to time schedules permitting little tolerance for marginal accomplishments. Shortcomings at any point threaten the success of the total program. To prevent, or at least to detect in time, shortcomings of this import is the prime and commanding responsibility of our Air Force management system. To make concurrency work requires the strictest attention to the prerogatives of sound management. Every step along the way must be monitored and controlled.

"In a way, it is somewhat like building a house," according to General Ritland. "The person who is designing it must have a keen ability to think dimensionally. Regardless of how carefully he draws his plans, though, it is almost inevitable that an unforeseen circumstance will crop up as the house takes shape in brick and mortar. Human nature being what it is, the builder may change his mind about the location of a room or closet when experience or closer study suggests to him a more efficient arrangement. But in building a ballistic missile base, design plans are not changed as a result of whim or fancy. Certain portions of the original design ideas may indeed be changed if the input from research and development and test indicates to the builder that greater economy or efficiency can be achieved by doing something a better way."

And this, returning now to General Bernard A. Schriever, was another reason for a second ICBM program: "The von Neumann Committee felt there should be two ICBM weapon systems to back up each other in the area of major subsystems— such as guidance, re-entry and propulsion techniques. We planned our TITAN Program in such a way that had we seriously run into any of these fundamental problems with the AT-LAS, we could have taken a subsystem developed in the TITAN and applied it to the ATLAS.

"In fact, we did just that in one important case. An all-inertial guidance system that was part of TITAN, we applied to the ATLAS Program. The ATLAS "E," which is the second configuration of ATLAS, has the inertial guidance system that originally started with TITAN."

DRAMATIC PROOF IN SECRET FLIGHT

It should be added that TITAN has since developed an even more advanced all-inertial guidance system for its second configuration. Both guidance systems, as I have earlier explained, cannot be jammed or diverted from their course by an enemy. They "think for themselves," requiring no ground direction by radio as did those in the earlier configurations of ATLAS and TITAN. Appropriately enough, they were pioneered by Dr. Charles S. Draper in MIT's Instrumentation Laboratory, where Colonel Paul Blasingame did research for his doctoral thesis in engineering. Not generally known is that a year before the Western Development Division was established, all-inertial guidance for ICBMs was proved dramatically in practice to be feasible. A cross-continent secret flight was made in 1953, using this type of guidance system in a B-29 Super Fortress. It took off from the Instrumentation Laboratory's flight-test facility in Massachusetts and was navigated by the system during the entire flight, until it approached within easy communication range of Los Angeles. Secrecy surrounding the flight was kept watertight throughout 4 years, until Dr. Draper himself disclosed certain of its details in 1957. This was only after the Air Force and the Laboratory had flight-tested the world's first transistorized (and therefore miniaturized) all-inertial system in a new, and then high-speed, jet fighter, the F-94C Starfire. This test of the system in actual flight showed conclusively that all-inertial guidance could be carried by an ICBM, so the earlier guidance system was unclassified with no fear that it would tip off an enemy to the capabilities of the newer system.

The approach is typical of all our security techniques: one system is downgraded and released publicly only after a much more advanced system of its kind has been developed to the point of realization. Thus, no matter how miraculous to the public a weapon or space system may seem to be, it is usually years behind a current system cloaked in secrecy.

Almost immediately after the Western Development Division was established, MIT's Instrumentation Laboratory was given a direct contract by WDD to develop an all-inertial guidance system for the experimental TITAN ICBM, then known only as WS-107A-2. Its operational missile designation for its ultimate user, the Strategic Air Command, still remained SM-68. The Air Force designation for the operational ATLAS was SM-65.

Odd as it may seem, however, the first strategic missile to fly with an all-inertial guidance system was SM-75. It was not an ICBM. It was the THOR Intermediate Range Ballistic Missile (IRBM), now deployed in England with the Royal Air Force as one part of the United States contribution to the armed strength of NATO. Development of the SM-75 THOR was added to WDD's projects in mid-December 1955. Secretary of Defense Wilson had announced this upcoming addition of IRBM Number One to the Air Force ballistic missile programs a month before the responsibility became official. The IRBM Program had a priority second only to that of the ICBMs. It called for operational capability by January 1960. The first operational version of THOR was launched at Cape Canaveral on November 5, 1958, after only eighteen research and development flight tests. Five other prior THOR flights were used to test Reentry Vehicle designs and to launch the world's first successful space probe, PIONEER I. The THOR IRBM was a year and a month early in completing its operational schedule. It was, of course, a much simpler missile than the ICBMs, but it did establish the correctness of many subsystem concepts, including all-inertial guidance. This was quite a victory for WDD.

The man that General Schriever chose as WDD's management executive for the ballistic missile Guidance and Control Department was Colonel Benjamin Paul Blasingame. He described for me the maneuver that ultimately made the controversial all-inertial guidance a respectable system to control the flight of ICBMs. As a result, our later model long-range missiles have the world's most lethally accurate and foolproof guidance. "At the outset of the ICBM Program there were enormous unknowns. And ignorance always causes you to try a lot of things, gives you a lot of worries. In the scientific community, the general feeling was that radar and radio techniques were indicated by enough evidence to be the logical techniques for the long-range guidance job. From the very outset of our program, these scientists felt strongly that we should commit the long-range missiles to radio guidance systems. We knew something about the accuracy of tracking radars. Assembling our knowledge, it could be clearly shown that we could do a fair guidance job using those known techniques. But another technique was just emerging from the laboratory at this time. It was the all-inertial system. Yet the fact of the matter is that it was discounted by the general scientific community. There were extremely strong opinions that this type of precise equipment could not be made to work in the very rough environment of a missile. Both the strong vibration and high acceleration we expected to have in an ICBM were against using such guidance equipment. The feeling against it was so *very* strong that we at WDD just barely convinced the scientific community that we ought to have an inertial system in development as a sort of back-up system. Our argument was that we might, if it proved itself in the process of development, be able to use it sometime in the future. Of course the inertial system was *very, very* attractive from a military standpoint. Here again I think is illustrated so clearly the importance of having military participation in the leadership management of scientific programs, along with the technical people. If the country took just the decisions of the engineers, the technical man's decisions, we wouldn't have followed through with the development of inertial guidance equipment. But it had such enormous potential military advantages that, indeed, we did very carefully include in the guidance-development program the creation of inertial systems.

"We had a strange opportunity to make our point. The apparent need for a shorter range strategic missile came up. It appeared that our allies should be provided with some additional strategic capability. Besides, many technical advisory sources argued that a medium-range ballistic missile would be easier to achieve than an ICBM. For example: You don't have to be as accurate in your control system; you don't have to be as accurate in your guidance; and the re-entry problem is of much less concern because the IRBM velocities are so much lower. If the ICBM program failed, it was reasoned, we would still have the IRBM.

COMMITMENT TO JAM-PROOF GUIDANCE

"So in the latter part of the Fall of 1955 we received a directive to start on a medium-range ballistic missile program. And I recall very well—it was on Christmas Day—working with our group, writing up the terms and conditions of the contract that we eventually placed with Douglas Aircraft. It was in this missile, the THOR, that we made our commitment to the inertial system as the primary technique of guidance.

"There was general belief that we could make it work, because at the shorter ranges the precision required for the control of an inertial platform was so much less. And so that's the way it was done. From the outset, we committed the THOR Program to inertial equipment and provided as back-up a radio guidance system."

In brief elaboration on Dr. Blasingame's story, three guidance systems were seriously considered for ICBMs by the technical advisors to WDD. Each had shortcomings but could be made to work. One was the "long baseline system," which would employ four separate tracking radars spaced anywhere from 10 to 50 miles apart. As the missile was acquired by each radar, it would then send its tracking information to a ground-based central computer. The electronic "brain" would then determine if the missile was on course and, if not, make corrections by radio to steer the ICBM back to a preplanned trajectory. In a second system a single central tracking radar was to follow the ICBM's positions in space, while information on the missile's velocity was obtained separately by analyzing the shifting energy of a radio signal emanating from it. Technically, this energy-shift is the well-known "Doppler Shift." The position and velocity information would be continuously combined in a computer so that proper steering signals could be sent back to the missile. A third system involved use of a single, highly precise tracking radar and a very elaborate computer. This computer would take the position information supplied by the radar and analyze it in terms of time. The time it took the bird to move from one small point in space to another was expressed in a mathematical equation wherein distance divided by time equalled velocity. Since velocity is never constant (actually it is a changing speed) the computer had quite a job to do with this guidance system. It had to remember the speed of the missile at one location (speed *is* a constant) while it compared such information with the missile's speed and location a fractional second later; it then calculated the difference in those two speeds. Simultaneously, it had to evaluate this difference against thousands of other speed differences from moment to moment so that it could know whether or not the bird was in the correct position at the correct velocity on its target course. If the bird was off course, the computer either had to subtract the deviation from or add it to the correct trajectory in order to know what radio signals to transmit for correction. No two targets are ever at exactly the same distance from a missile launch position. Each requires a different trajectory for achievement of a strike. Even if this were to be measured in the minutest differences of altitude and direction, the velocity and spatial positions of an ICBM must be rigidly controlled during the powered phases of flight.

A major part of this problem is eliminated with an all-inertial guidance system, which carries its own computer inside the missile.

None of the three early ICBM guidance methods were considered basically attractive from the military point of view. The long baseline system cost too much money—too much real estate was required in order to set up the sequence of tracking radars for each missile squadron. Each of numerous tracts of real estate would have to be tightly security-controlled, thus adding further expense. The second guidance system was too complex for thorough reliability. The third system, although self-contained, was equally complex. All three systems would have been vulnerable to electronic counter-measures by an enemy. Yet they were the most practical approaches based on existing experience of the period. In fact, the latter two systems were finally developed to a high state of reliability for the early ATLAS and TITAN I respectively, but they could still be jammed electronically. The most effective strategic deterrent is a foolproof weapon that can strike fast, accurately and deep into the enemy's homeland when necessary.

As General Schriever so aptly puts it today: "During the early stages of World War II, the Germans referred to their mobile warfare as *Blitzkrieg* or "lightning war." By this they meant that fast-moving, motorized columns might penetrate, envelop and obtain a decision in a few days or a few weeks, depending on the depth of territory to be secured and the forces defending it. In the present era a well-coordinated attack by ballistic missiles might obtain a decision in less than an hour—or in several hours if the outcome waited for follow-up strikes and counter-assaults by missiles and aircraft. Depth of territory is a factor of no consequence to the intercontinental missile. Since the distance traveled is governed by cutoff velocity of the rocket engine and trajectory angle of the missile, time in flight is nearly the same, whether the missile covers 5,000 miles or 9,000 miles or more."

ICBM SECRECY PARTIALLY UNCOVERED

Yet in those early days when General Schriever commanded a Division that was housed in an abandoned parochial school, he could never have made the foregoing statement in any way that would reach the public. The words "ballistic" and "missile" were purposely not even included in the name of his Division, secretive as that was. When finally the Western Development Division was renamed the Air Force Ballistic Missile Division on June 1, 1957, at least a part of the secrecy had been pared away. Superficial aspects of the ICBM Program could no longer be hidden. Success was imminent. Ten days later the first ATLAS was launched. Anybody who lived in a cottage on Cocoa Beach, Florida, could observe this huge monster spewing flame and smoke as it rose slowly above Cape Canaveral.

The citizenry of Inglewood, California, however, had had no such visible sign that anything unusual was going on right in their midst. The old parochial school, abandoned because it was not sufficiently modern, was located right in the center of busy little Inglewood. It consisted of a cluster of three buildings—a brick schoolhouse and two wooden frame buildings, the chapel and recreation hall.

Dr. Blasingame recalls the chapel with a fond nostalgia. "We made full use of that chapel," he told me. "At first we used it as an auditorium to hold our conferences and make presentations when we had to communicate with large groups of people —for instance, when we called in contractors for a briefing on what we wanted them to bid on. We used to say that it was a good thing some of that early work on the program was done in the chapel because it restrained us from outbursts over frustrations—and there were many. I remember we later installed a number of partitions in the chapel and used to kid our contractors by saying that we had confessional booths when we needed them to get to the bottom of any of our troubles. The partitioned rear of the chapel actually became our electronic computing center. It was the only air-conditioned part of the place. So I guess that this was the first time in history that anybody had ever set up an electronically controlled chapel.

"Just what was going on in our little complex was a great mystery to everybody in the neighborhood. We got this impression from our secretaries (by that time we had acquired secretaries) who didn't know what we were doing either. Across the street from us there was a typical little Los Angeles open-air hot dog stand and the secretaries, who were security-cleared for a military job, began to call that place the "Officers Club." It was where we officers always ate lunch and very frequently dinner, when we could find the time to get out and do it. Lunch was probably the only time we ever got out into the sunshine of California."

The Inglewood Complex today is about 4 miles west of the old parochial school and consists of at least twenty stone and concrete buildings very modern in design. The new Officers Club has an eye-appealing comfortable lounge, restaurant and bar. But the officers, following tradition, often still wear civilian clothes.

Again to quote Frank Burnham: "It's a holdover from the fact that when this organization was established, civilian clothes were the order of the day. Nowadays, except when our people are traveling on duty as official representatives of the Air Force, or except when they are hosts here to official dignitaries or personnel from the other military services, you'll seldom see them in uniform. Normally, you can't tell our colonels from our captains and you can't tell the colonels and captains from the civilian scientists employed by Aerospace and STL."

Burnham's references are to the Aerospace Corporation and Space Technology Laboratories. STL evolved from the original Ramo-Wooldridge Corporation as a nonprofit engineering advisor to the Air Force. The Aerospace Corporation succeeded STL as the most recent, most advanced nonprofit civilian scientific and technical organization to consult on far-out military space projects, while STL continued to work for the Air Force as a regular contractor in ballistic missile programs. In line with the magnitude and urgency of the present task (which will be elaborated upon in Chapter Six) the Air Research and Development Command of USAF was completely reorganized and streamlined into the Systems Command. Appropriately, as part of the reorganization, the military managerial body has been split into two organizations and their self-descriptive names have been changed from Ballistic Missile Division to Space Systems Division and Ballistic Systems Division. Their evolution directly from the Western Development Division is a symbol of the farsightedness and courage of a small group of men who refused to admit that anything was impossible. With that attitude they laid down the firmest foundation for the Space Age in America, both military and civilian. For the civilian Space Administration could not have successfully orbited on schedule their Mercury Astronauts without the use of ATLAS ICBMs as rocket boosters. Many future civilian space research projects will depend upon the TITAN ICBM. The THOR IRBM as well has provided the Space Administration with an invaluable rocket booster for scientific space research. Among its achievements for the civilian NASA have been the successful orbiting of the 100-foot-diameter Echo I Satellite and the space-probe PIONEER V, which proved that interplanetary radio communication is possible by two-way communication with the Earth from a distance of about 22,500,000 miles.

MILITARY-INDUSTRIAL TEAMWORK

None of these, along with numerous other spectacular events that have changed the whole future of the human race for the better, would have been possible without the dedicated military-industrial teamwork first conceived and vigorously sponsored by the Western Development Division of the United States Air Force. Men of the WDD believed implicitly in the genius of American free-enterprise industry to get a herculean job done in time to maintain national superiority of strategic power, and thus national security.

The approach used by the Air Force was a radical departure from the so-called "arsenal concept" of the other military departments. Traditionally, the Army and Navy engineered their own weapons and then gave blueprints to industry for production. But with the advent of a need for vast, unprecedented weapon systems, the Air Force men of vision saw that the traditional approach would restrict progress. There simply would never be a sufficient number of scientific and engineering personnel in the military to handle alone the design and development of "Buck Rogers weapons," as many called them in the early days. So the concept of military scientific and technical management supported by skilled as well as unbiased civilian advice came into being. The specific requirements of a new weapon system were conceived by this team, then turned over to industry for elaboration and development. Competitive industrial firms would then match their experience, imagination and production resources one against another to propose the best possible way to meet those requirements. In this manner, the Air Force was able to utilize the nation's best creative scientific, engineering and production talents. Genuine cooperation between the Air Force and industry was the cornerstone of success. When that success became evident, the Army and Navy began to discard the old arsenal concept and develop a military-industrial approach as well. The civilian National Aeronautics and Space Administration, from its beginning, has used a similar NASA-industry approach. But it can fairly be said that the Air Force pointed the way as an only means to meet schedules on a DX Priority for long-range ballistic missiles.

That Priority demanded simultaneous action on many technological fronts, as has already been stated. While alternate missiles and guidance systems were on the drawing boards, full-speed activity was in progress to develop rocket engines and Re-entry Vehicles with warhead-protective materials that would not be vaporized by friction with the atmosphere. General Electric Company and the AVCO Corporation had contracts to develop the RVs and were experimenting with two extremely different techniques. The GE method was based on a copper "heat-sink." Copper is a metal that radiates heat almost as rapidly as it is heated. The idea here was that a copper RV would swiftly soak up and cast away the heat from instant to instant as it descended through ever-thickening levels of air. The AVCO approach made use of ablative materials—that is, materials that would peel away from the RV at certain critical temperatures and thus carry off the heat step by step in successive layers of the material. The temperature realm involved with re-entry had a peak of about 14,000° Fahrenheit. As experimental models of the RVs became available they were tested in actual flight conditions by Lockheed, which had developed a three-stage solid-fuel rocket designated by the Air Force as "X-17." The X-17 simulated re-entry temperatures by taking the test RV as high as its first stage could soar, then by turning the second and third stages downward the RV was accelerated back into the atmosphere at high velocities. Later, a few of the RV tests at ICBM ranges were accomplished with a THOR. The ultimate choice for use on ICBMs was in favor of the AVCO ablative technique, since it was more efficient. The copper used by GE had added excessive weight to the Re-entry Vehicle.

Two companies were also working on different approaches to all-inertial guidance. One was American Bosch-Arma, the other was the AC Sparkplug Division of General Motors. Both systems were intended as possibilities for an advanced version of the TITAN ICBM. As it turned out, both were perfected. Thus, the ATLAS "E" Model was given the Bosch-Arma system, to make it practically invulnerable.

Meanwhile, North American Aviation had been carrying forth research and development work on the NAVAHO, a cruise-type intercontinental missile. Although this missile was forced to fly within a comparatively low part of the atmosphere because it was propelled by an air-breathing ramjet engine, it did have a huge booster to send it aloft at ramjet speeds. (There is a critical speed in relationship to altitude at which a ramjet operates. It is not a self-starting engine.) The booster was a pure rocket. Eventually, the NAVAHO Program was dropped, but the booster engine was scaled out to provide the three basic power plants of ATLAS. It also supplied the rocket engine for THOR.

Rocket engines for the TITAN ICBM were being developed by the Aerojet-General Corporation. These were ready when TITAN I was ready for captive testing.

FIRST UNDERGROUND PROTECTED MISSILE

The TITAN program undoubtedly contributed more to the art of intercontinental missilery than any other program—but this was expected. Probably the most incredible part of that program was its hard-site aspect. TITAN was the first ICBM conceived as a weapon system to be protected by underground storage and launch. The man who conceived of the hard site for TITAN was Colonel Blasingame. By that time he had been transferred from the Guidance and Control Department to become the first Director of the entire TITAN program. His own words will be much more adequate than mine to describe the situation.

"All of our missile programs," he recalled, "were scheduled and designed to be what we would today call 'soft installations.' That means the launcher was designed to be installed above ground, that the missile was expected to be *stored* above ground. Now first of all, part of the reasoning for this was that it seemed the easiest thing to do—and secondly, we didn't think of doing anything else. After all, the manned aircraft operated from the surface of the ground, and we thought very frequently in comparative terms, comparing the missile system with manned aircraft.

"But as I thought more and more about this, I realized that it was basically in error. Missiles and aircraft *are* different—and you should design an operational system to exploit these differences. Certainly you have to design your operational set-up in recognition of these differences. So mentally starting with an evaluation of the original concept of a soft installation, I reached the *very, very firm* conviction that a missile system that was not given some additional protection to enhance its survivability would be a relatively useless device.

"In other words, the missile *had* to be set up operationally so that it could survive an initial attack because you simply cannot launch the missile in retaliation until you know *positively* that you *have* been attacked. On the other hand, with manned aircraft—and this is one of their great virtues—you can take off when you get any *indication* that you are under attack. For example, when you detect some unknown targets on radar away up at the DEW Line or detect the same thing on the large BMEWS radars, you can launch your airplanes, send them off, get them started on the way to their targets. You're in constant communication with them. If the attack is real, you can give them the word to go ahead. If not, they will return. Well, this is a choice that you do not have with a missile. And thinking about this vital difference drove me to the conclusion that the missile *had to be treated separately.*

"So against rather general opposition, I undertook a campaign to redevelop the parts of the TITAN System so that it could be converted for use in a hardened operational site. And this I would list as probably my own personal major contribution to the program.

"Now I don't want to sound so darned wise either. It was not just myself, of course. . . ."

I interrupted with a question. "There was general opposition, even at this point in the program?"

Dr. Blasingame nodded. "The real opposition, strangely enough, came from our own technical people. They recognized that we were grossly ignorant of what it might take to harden a missile base, to give it really effective protection against ground shock and against the very high overpressures that would be experienced from a nearby atomic or H-bomb blast. In addition to the heavy technical opposition internally, there was a lot of scoffing by some of our military people. They said that this new problem, the development of a hard-site, would make the program so late that it would become unattractive—and this *was* a very real worry.

"As I started to say, it was not just myself who was for the hardened missile bases. I always discovered when I went to the boss with an idea that he was several jumps ahead of me. When I went to Bernie Schriever with this idea, I found that he had

thought about it very carefully six months earlier than I had. So
as soon as I told him how very strongly I felt that we needed to
do this, to convert the whole program to hardened sites, I discovered that he had already reached this same conclusion. I enjoyed his complete support from the very first day."

General Schriever's support in reorienting the TITAN Program wove a chain of technological events without precedent in
military history. The design and development of underground
hardened ICBM sites strained the creativity and physical
stamina of all concerned—the Air Force, the technical advisors
and industry. Involved were a range of "unknowns" that
equalled those that had to be discovered and conquered in per-
fecting the long-range missiles themselves. The construction
task transcended almost anything ever attempted by mankind.
For here, too, there was a compression of time. Tolerating no
delays in the TITAN Program, the Air Force demanded that
the hard sites be perfected and ready on exactly the same
schedule as the missiles. In fact, the hard-site development,
starting late, had to catch up with and surpass the missile development. If TITAN was to be mated successfully with its
hardened site, the site had to be ready, at least in prototype
operational form, for launch-and-flight-testing.

An intensive series of studies was begun. Consideration was
even given to the use of abandoned mine shafts and caverns inside mountains. But protecting the missile in such ways had to
be discarded. A vitally important aspect of the hardened ICBM
squadrons was that they had to be dispersed in locations that
would make their targets in the Soviet Union easily accessible,
while they themselves were inaccessible to an enemy. Another
factor that determined location was safety of the North American population: if the missiles ever had to be fired in anger,
their trajectories should not take them over heavily populated
areas. It was a mammoth project.

The decisions were finally made in favor of two kinds of hard
site—again, the backup approach for insurance. The first of
these was an elevator system that lifted the TITAN out of its

reinforced underground hole to the surface for launching. The second was an in-silo launch technique, whereby the ICBM was fired directly out of the concrete-and-steel-protected hole in which it was stored.

ARMY-AIR FORCE COOPERATION

A cooperative arrangement was made by the Air Force with the United States Army Corps of Engineers to proceed with the hard-site construction. Simultaneously, construction was begun across the nation, including the prototype test-and-training sites at Vandenberg Air Force Base, California. At the same time, major electronic and mechanical systems and sub-systems for the sites were being developed, tested and manu-factured. The schedule for completion on an operational basis for all sites with missiles installed was set for no later than year's end of 1963. "Herculean" is a small word to depict the task.

"Somehow, without prejudicing security restrictions, we must find a way to acquaint the American public with that per-formance," said Major General Alvin C. Welling in reference to the task. General Welling was placed in command of the or-ganization that managed all site construction, the Army's Corps of Engineers Construction Agency. Agreeing with him thoroughly, I'll try to do as he suggested.

Most of the structure of the hard sites is buried in the ground. The only visible markers are heavy slabs of concrete, flush with the landscape, surrounded by grass and barbed-wire fencing. These fence-enclosed slabs spot every conceivable type of countryside from East to West and from the desert to the Far North.

The slabs are really thick concrete doors weighing anywhere from 80 to 400 tons each, depending upon the type of missile that lies beneath them. For although the hard-site concept came out of the TITAN ICBM program, research and development in that program have made hardened sites possible for both later model ATLAS ICBMs and all the models of MINUTE-MAN, the three-stage solid-fueled ICBM. The slabs are the launch doors guarding these missiles, ready to open for their release at a given command. The slabs are also the only surface indication of vast underground "cities" connected by steel-walled tunnels and heavy electrical cables. Each city has its own power generators, food and water supplies, sleeping and work quarters, a center for medical care, a warehouse for supplies—and a targeting room. This last is Top Secret. In it are filed the coded instructions that pinpoint an enemy strategic target 6,000 miles away, or farther. The city is also hardened.

What does hardened really mean? Briefly, it means that the buried city with its squadron of deadly missiles has been designed and built to withstand all but a direct hit by an enemy. Even with a direct hit, it might survive. For example, the blast overpressure from a 10-megaton H-bomb exploded on the ground 5-miles away would be a fraction over 7 pounds per square inch, or enough to shake apart the average brick office building. The earlier missile hard sites can withstand pressures up to 100 pounds against every square inch of structure. The later sites have been improved to withstand an even greater blast. Semi-hard sites—an interim development which took place while the true hard sites were being developed—can easily take 25 pounds of pressure per square inch. These are popularly called a "coffin configuration" by the ICBM technical people, since in them an ATLAS lies horizontally with a long slab covering it. ATLAS is erected to a vertical launch-position as the slab rolls away. In this semi-hard site the missile is closer to the surface than in the true hard site, where the missiles stand vertically within a silo-like structure.

To knock out a semi-hard site would take a 10-megaton surface blast as close as 2¾ miles away. The fully hardened site could withstand the same blast effects as close as 1⅖ miles. Doubling an H-bomb's power does not automatically double its destructive potency. The hardened underground city could survive 20 megatons exploding less than 1⅘ miles away.

But Mr. Khrushchev boasts of 50- and 100-megaton bombs. Even if he could deliver them to the target locality, they would have to strike within a 2- and 3-mile radius of dead center, the hard site. That's a lot of accuracy to hang your hopes on in a single, double or even triple long-range shot. An H-bomb bursting in the air is more deadly than one exploding on the ground. It would create an additional 20 to 30 pounds of blast overpressure per square inch, if it were at a certain optimum height. Notwithstanding the delicate timing devices such a burst would demand, Mr. Khrushchev would still have to strike a hairsbreadth under 2 miles from his target to destroy the earlier-type hard site with a 20-megaton yield.

This project to have all hard sites combat-ready on a crash basis was officially designated the Site-Activation Program. The boss of that total program was Lieutenant General Thomas Patrick Gerrity. At the time he wore the two stars of a major general. He managed the program with such drive and efficiency that he is now the Air Force Deputy Chief of Staff for Systems and Logistics in the Pentagon.

General Gerrity is the kind of person who hates to be tough, yet tough he was—to the point where he made impossible demands everywhere he went. And he went everywhere—to Cape Canaveral, where the missiles were being perfected in flight tests; to the training and test center at Vandenberg AFB, where the perfected missiles were being test-mated with their silos and combat crews were being trained in maintenance and launch techniques; to every ATLAS, TITAN and MINUTEMAN site, where construction was in progress; to all of the associate contractors and the hundreds of subcontractors involved in the inconceivably vast program to merge thousands of big and and little components into a workable system.

He made the rounds, from coast to coast, at least once a month, sometimes more often as the need arose. Traveling by air on a circuit of the sites alone required 8,000 miles of flying.

TITANIC ENGINEERING TASK

Before General Curtis LeMay, Air Force Chief of Staff, called in Thomas Patrick Gerrity and gave him full authority to manage the program, it was slipping for a number of reasons. Among the minor ones were labor disputes and strikes. The major reason was the titanic multiple-engineering task that required a combat time schedule and precision of components that often required tolerances in hundreds of millionths of an inch. These components were produced at different locations throughout the nation and had to match perfectly when finally installed at an isolated site in the wilderness.

Altogether, 23 ICBM bases were planned, extending from New York to California and from the Canadian to the Mexican borders. Some of the bases contained more than one missile squadron and therefore more than one hard site. The sites themselves are scattered through an area of about 100,000 square miles of the United States. The smallest, a TITAN I squadron of nine missiles plus a spare, is located at Larson Air Force Base in the State of Washington. It is 970 square miles, or four-fifths the area of Rhode Island. The largest, a wing of 150 MINUTE-MAN ICBMs, is dispersed throughout 20,000 square miles among the mountain ranges of Montana. The area of this missile wing is twice that of Maryland. Others are located throughout the boulders of Idaho, the crags of Wyoming, the mesas of Utah, the rocky deserts of Arizona, the sands of New Mexico, the plateaus of Colorado, the Great Plains of Kansas, Nebraska and Iowa, the oil-rich vastness of Texas, the hills of Oklahoma. There is one site in Northern New York. Two are in California.

Naturally, a missile that flies in a test launch would appear to be a more spectacular achievement than digging holes in the ground to contain it. Yet those "holes" are equally spectacular. No other holes like these have ever before been dug.

More than 26,000,000 cubic yards of earth, mostly in difficult terrain, had to be moved for the launch sites. According to General Welling, "This is enough earth to build a levee 5 feet high and 10 feet wide for the entire length of the Mississippi River." The excavation and construction job gathers added color as the General makes a few other comparisons: "The more than 3,000-

000 cubic yards of concrete poured is about the same as the concrete content of the Hoover Dam, or enough to build a 20-foot-wide highway between Los Angeles and Topeka, Kansas.

"Almost a million passenger automobiles could be built with the 764,000 tons of steel required. This is enough to provide tracks for a railroad running from Los Angeles to Washington, D.C. and from there down to Cape Canaveral, off Cocoa Beach, Florida."

Air Force Colonel William D. Alexander, Assistant Deputy Commander for Facilities at the then new Ballistic Systems Division, tosses in several of his own comparisons: "Each of the nine missile silos required for one TITAN operational squadron has an inside diameter of 40 feet and is deep enough to enclose a fifteen-story building. Some 12,000 tons of piping is installed in every squadron in addition to nearly 2,000,000 pounds of stainless steel. There are 10,000 feet of tunnel, 570 miles of electrical wiring and three underground powerhouses, each of a size sufficient to serve a city of 5,000 population."

It should also be mentioned that construction of these underground missile-launching centers was accomplished in both geographic and weather extremes. Work went on at highest priority in the baked and windy deserts of the Southwest, the steamy rains of the Deep South, the almost unbearable heat near the Mexican border and the almost unbearable cold near the Midwestern and Northwestern Canadian borders. At the Great Falls, Montana, ICBM site, the winter temperatures often drop to 42° below zero Fahrenheit. At the Tucson, Arizona, site, the summer temperatures climb as high as 110° Fahrenheit.

Yet not only was work continued on an urgent schedule around the year, but the construction task alone was "being performed with the explosive speed of a combat operation complicated by the requirement for the delicate precision of an instrument laboratory," says Army General Welling.

And Air Force General Gerrity justifies the $15,000,000,000 cost of the total ICBM Program, including the Site-Activation Program, in the following manner. We were facing each other across a long conference table in his former large, efficient-looking office at the Inglewood Complex when I asked him for the justification. His expression had been relaxed, but now his facial muscles tightened as he leaned forward with clenched fists on the table. He spoke distinctly and determinedly. "For the American family, it buys peace. It buys a mighty deterrent to war. In my opinion, these are worth a much higher price than fifteen billion dollars. They're worth a price that we can't afford *not* to pay."

Despite all the squabbles, statements and misstatements, labor disputes and strikes, reorganizations and Congressional hearings behind closed and open doors, the hardened underground sites and the continent-spanning missiles that are a lethal part of the system have converged in their development to meet a schedule that must be considered historic in the annals of technology.

Out of that schedule have come new Strategic Air Command designations for the missiles. TITAN is now "HSM-68" for Hardened Strategic Missile-68. ATLAS is either "HSM-65" or "CSM-65," the latter for Coffin-based Strategic Missile-65. Every MINUTEMAN ICBM is HSM-80.

"Today, not even the most boastful Russian rocket-rattler asserts that the Soviet Union has the nuclear power to destroy the United States." That was the Honorable Robert S. McNamara speaking in Chicago on February 17, 1962, at a dinner sponsored by the Fellows of the American Bar Association. The Defense Secretary also warned that "over the next several years" the Soviets will develop an intercontinental ballistic missile force.

But Mr. Khrushchev rattles his big rockets anyway—before the fact. He claims that he is holding over our heads a "Sword of Damocles," his much-publicized 50- and 100-megaton super H-bombs. How seriously should we take Mr. K's threat? Is it merely a boast based on the Ancient Greek legend of the flatterer Damocles, who was finally punished by Dionysius by the command that he sit at a banquet with a sword dangling over his head supported only by a single hair? Or does Khru-shchev really have the horrendous power of destruction he claims, balanced so delicately above the roof of every American home?

RELIABILITY AND ACCURACY BOTH REQUIRED

Whether or not he has those superbombs, no matter how ter-rifying they may be in destructive force, he *must* be *certain* that he can deliver them reliably and accurately on target across con-tinents—if he doesn't want sure and massive retaliation. At one time, such accuracy was not a requirement—if the Communists wanted only to terrorize us into subjection. They had only to hit one of our big cities in a surprise attack. Today they know that before their missiles could carry Khrushchev's huge bombs to zero in on American cities, they would first have to knock out every hardened ICBM site in the United States. This would al-most certainly be impossible. For one thing, it would bankrupt the Kremlin economically. To be absolutely sure of knocking out every single ICBM hard site, the Kremlin could not depend upon even the highest kind of missile accuracy. Our sites are widely dispersed for a purpose—to make an enemy long-range missile attack infeasible, economically as well as militarily. It should take at least a dozen Red ICBMs to inactivate the con-trol center of a single hardened squadron of ours, and this is giv-ing the Reds a big benefit of the doubt regarding their accu-racy. Inactivating all of our hardened ICBM squadrons and wings (to play it safe, if the control centers should be missed) should require 14,000 or more Red long-range missiles—all of them highly reliable as well as accurate. Conservatively, not in-cluding the price of operational support equipment or hardened launch-sites, such an attack would cost the Russian Communists about $30 billions.

For precisely this reason, to checkmate whatever ICBM as-pirations the Russians may have, the Western Development Division was established and assigned a DX Priority. The unbelievably successful execution of that Priority resulted from a rare species of man.

It did not matter whether he was a captain or a colonel, as Frank Burnham suggests. Nor did it matter if he were a civilian employed by the Air Force or industry. All that mattered was that he have the ability to think clearly, unhampered by tradition or prejudice, and to make firm decisions on his conclusions, regardless of how controversial those decisions might be. Another characteristic of the species was a strong drive to accomplish the "impossible."

When Colonel Blasingame reluctantly left the TITAN Program before its completion, he did so for three reasons. First, the Air Force Academy had just been founded, and Major General James E. Briggs, Academy Superintendent, in a search for men of outstanding qualities of leadership and talent came upon Blasingame's record. He was requested to head the Department of Astronautics, or Spaceflight. The fact that such a Department existed was a tribute to the work of WDD, which had come into being only 4 years earlier. Second, General Schriever advised Blasingame to accept the new post, since he felt that the Colonel would be of inestimable value in the training of future Air Force spacemen. Third, the man chosen to replace Colonel Blasingame as Director of the TITAN Program impressed him deeply. That man was Colonel Albert "Red" Wetzel.

"When I met Colonel Wetzel," Dr. Blasingame told me, "I *knew* that I could forget everything I ever did—and he would take care of things as I would myself. There was no one I ever met, other than Wetzel, who felt as closely as I did about the TITAN Program. I knew I was leaving it in the best possible hands. So I left with a clear conscience."

Wetzel, a jet bomber pilot in SAC, was also experienced in missilery. During the early days (1947 through 1952) before the ICBM era, he had successively been Project Officer on development of the Martin-Matador—America's first operational guided missile—and Chief of the Atomic Warheads Branch for Guided Missiles. Among his other talents, Colonel Wetzel brought to the TITAN Program a sense of humor.

"When you're driving to get a job done," he once said to me, "not very many people like you, but they respect you and that's all I ask."

They respected him so much that he was forced even to work in his sleep. Here's how he put it: "Those people in Washington, at the Pentagon or the Systems Command, they get to work at seven or eight o'clock. First thing you know, they have a problem. So they grab the phone and they call me, never stopping to think that out here in California it's four or five o'clock in the morning. I grab the phone, dazed and bleary and hear someone say, 'Hey, Red, whaddya do if there's a lox-fill overflow on the blasphemous bleeder?'—or some such silly question. Before I'm awake enough to get sore, I've answered the guy and gone back to sleep."

DEADLY SERIOUS HUMOR

The Colonel's sense of humor, however, has a deadly serious foundation. He assigned a captain to the most important managerial position on the TITAN program, apart from his own position. He knew that the seriousness and dedication of this man were more valuable than rank. This captain was always finding fault with the Air Force TITAN management structure. Wetzel finally told him that "The guy that complains about the food, always winds up as mess officer" and appointed him Executive Officer on the Program. It was Captain Bill Dean.

Captain Dean, to use his own phrase, set himself up as "a devil's advocate." He made it a point always to take the unpopular view in order to make the others continually re-evaluate the validity of their approach to problems. "I had laid out for myself the task of taking the opposite side of every picture, of trying to convince all the others that they did not yet know what the total job was. This kept them trying to convince me that they did know and in so doing they either saw the loopholes of their reasoning or were more clearly convinced they were right."

It was easier to be wrong than right in those early days of long-range missile development, yet everybody *had* to be right if the big missiles were to become operational on schedule. Colonel Wetzel devised a little parable that he often tossed at his men. "You're out hunting alligators," he said, "so watch yourself. It's not only that great big mouth full of teeth that you have to worry about—it's that great big horny tail that'll whip around when you're not looking and knock you on your posterior!"

Because of these attitudes the TITAN finally became the mightiest missile in the operational inventory of the Strategic Air Command.

Midway in the Program, Frank Burnham could write (and I quote verbatim from his personal notes, with his kind permission) that "the TITAN also represents an 'advanced ICBM.' While it was begun as part of a 'dual approach to the requirement for an ICBM,' it has forged ahead of its sister missile, taking advantage of lessons learned with the other program. Its range will be in excess of 5,500 nautical miles; its speed greater than 15,000 miles per hour. This can be translated into an ability to carry the same load farther and faster or a greater load the same distance and speed as the ATLAS."

The note was referring to TITAN I. The military-industrial team that brought this missile to operational status out of sweat and stubbornness, next moved toward the considerably more advanced TITAN II as well as toward TITAN III, which is unique in the TITAN family because it is not a weapon system but was designed specifically as an ultrareliable vehicle to launch a great variety of satellites and space probes. TITAN II is unparalleled in the Free World as a weapon system, but it is also helping to make possible another "impossible" schedule—the civilian program to land men safely on the moon before the decade's end. TITAN III will be unparalleled in determining whether democracy is to live in the future or not.

Two diametrically opposed social systems are involved in that determination—free enterprise, of course, and definitely communism. What are the odds in favor of free enterprise?

5.

A NEW KIND
of PHILOSOPHY

"Today the companies making up the United States aerospace industry represent the largest and most effective assembly of scientific and engineering talent in the Free World. They are specialists in the impossible.

"This capability did not evolve overnight. The well-spring for this competence is the private enterprise system that has generated industrial creativity."

—*Dan A. Kimball, former Secretary of the Navy, presently Member of the Board of Governors, Aerospace Industries Association.*

A T ONE time in the annals of human endeavor, philosophy was the sole province of introspective thinkers —men who derived their truths from basic assumptions that had not been proved in truth. As our scientific-industrial age grew in complexity, philosophy was thrust into a new mold, the mold of detached reasoning. Basic truths about nature were still inferred—but they had to be proved by experiment. The province of philosophy was transferred in a revolutionary way to scientists, engineers and managers. The latter, in fact, had to acquire the broadest objective view because they were at the apex of each pyramidal project and would topple if they didn't.

The astuteness of managerial philosophy is tested nowadays by the success of scientific endeavors and the quality of industrial products. Vast projects have sprung from the conflict inherent in opposing international policies. National prestige and

153

new scientific knowledge are involved with landing an American crew on the moon before the end of this decade. National survival—which includes survival of the Free World—is involved in the rapid development of modern detection-alarm, command-and-control and weapon systems.

Both kinds of involvement contribute to the strength and credibility of U.S. National Policies before the whole world. Both kinds demand the most rigorous and most imaginative approach to management on the parts of Government and industry.

The previous chapter told the story of Air Force management of what was perhaps the most ambitious military-scientific-industrial project recorded to date. It was, as the reader now knows, a project claimed to be impossible of attainment. That it was successfully accomplished is due in equal part to the managerial skills and resiliency of industry. The next chapter tells that part of the story.

Obviously, it would be not only impossible but unwieldy and confusing to portray the capabilities of all of the industrial organizations which contributed to America's ICBM deterrent strength. Each in its own way has a colorful history and symbolizes the determined managerial foresight that a freely competitive society requires for the survival and growth of any profit-motivated organization.

Among the classical examples, General Dynamics/Astronautics had the will, foresight and ingenuity to pursue concepts of spaceflight during a period when most big corporations were unwilling to risk their time and engineering talents in what was then considered a "crackpot" venture. As a result of GDA's enthusiasm and deep interest, the United States achieved ATLAS, the Free World's first ICBM and a workhorse rocket booster for scientific and manned space missions that, in addition to numerous other successes, made it possible for the United States to place men in orbit less than a half-dozen years after the Age of Space began with Sputnik I.

North American Aviation is another example of a genuinely

pioneering corporation that transcended the *status quo* of big industry by investing effort and money in visionary pursuits. They developed the first successful large liquid-fuel rocket engines with a power beyond that of the German V-2 engine. Their Redstone engine reliably sent the first American into space. Today, they are the industrial manager of the National Aeronautics and Space Administration's vastly ambitious engineering project to land men safely on the moon and bring them back to Earth before the end of this decade.

There are a number of others that deserve appreciative recognition by the public: Reaction Motors, Incorporated and the Aerojet-General Corporation are two that began on a gamble of funds, a rugged belief that man's future lay beyond the Earth's atmosphere and a refusal to be discouraged by failure after failure of many of their early ideas. RMI was founded with the life-savings of four men—a subway conductor, an adding machine serviceman and two young engineers. It amounted to a little more than $5,000. Aerojet-General was launched with $2,000 provided by Andrew G. Haley, then a young Army major and now internationally known as a legal adviser in telecommunications and spaceflight. These two companies today are, of course, great corporations and leaders in rocket propulsion as well as in a variety of associated scientific fields. RMI produced the engine that propelled a man through the sound-barrier in level flight for the first time. Their succeeding rocket engines have thrust men higher and faster than any human has ever flown in a winged aircraft. As one of a large number of achievements, Aerojet-General developed the AEROBEE, first rocket in the world to carry living creatures, mice and monkeys, into space and bring them back to Earth alive.

The Lockheed Missiles and Space Company, the Boeing Company, Douglas Aircraft and Bell Aerospace Corporation also were important pioneers in rocketry, as were General Electric, Hughes Aircraft and Northrop. All are now among the leaders of their industry.

Each of the foregoing organizations has a history of high

drama and determination. Each is presently engaged in exotic developmental work vital to the national defense as well as to the scientific benefit of mankind. Each would provide fascinating reading if its story were told in detail. But each of their stories would require a whole book. So I have been forced to be ruthlessly selective in my choice of an industrial organization that would demonstrate the acute managerial insights of men in the aerospace industry.

One company stood out as an ultimate choice because its many-faceted aspects—historically, technologically and managerially—fully reflect the capabilities and problems of almost every single aspect of the aerospace industry. In fact, the founder of this company was directly responsible for the encouragement of several aeronautical geniuses who, after acquiring experience with him, went on to found their own great pioneering companies. He was Glenn L. Martin. Two of his outstanding protégés were Larry Bell and Donald Douglas.

As one of the foremost contributors to the United States defense effort, the Martin Marietta Corporation appeared to me to be a graphic example of what free men can accomplish against tremendous odds, economic as well as scientific. Broadly based in nearly every important engineering field and type of scientific research, pure and applied alike, this company has led the way toward conquering many of the "impossibles" of our aerospace era. They have developed and produced nuclear powerplants for satellites and remotely situated radar stations, the first big rocket of American design for probing the secrets of the upper atmosphere, the first missile weapon system in the United States, the first multistage, rigid-frame and hardened ICBM, the first air-to-ground missile that requires no checkout equipment because of its reliability and storability, the first big tactical field ballistic missile with variable range, and the first rocket to combine in its stages the basic propulsion systems of the past decade-plus—liquid-cryogenic, liquid-hypergolic and solid propellants.

They have also helped to conceive and are now developing the first standardized military launch-vehicle to place a variety of heavy payloads in Earth-orbit or on the moon and planets. This company was not only a pioneer in space-scientific research and electronic guidance systems, but today they produce a greater variety of missile-types than any other in the industry. One-third of all test missiles and research rockets launched at Cape Canaveral since 1950 have been Martin-made.

Because of managerial philosophy and foresight, their range of scientific and engineering disciplines sweeps across all those vital not only to national defense but to national economic well-being. Among these are radiophysics, solid-state and aerospace physics, nucleonics, electronics, metallurgy, propulsion, chemistry, the biological sciences, optics and advanced mathematics, to name only a few.

The company's managerial philosophy is implicit in a statement of William B. Bergen, President of the Martin Company Division. Mr. Bergen was introduced in Chapter Three, where I interviewed him about the PERSHING Missile.

"It is no longer sufficient to stay on a par with your potential enemy," said Bergen recently. "The only safe way is to stay at least one step ahead of him to insure national survival. And, quite clearly, a second-best defense could be worse than no defense at all.

"Defense companies may study the Government's requirements and anticipate them, but studies do them little good unless they also have the capability of delivering, both in terms of facilities and in terms of talents. We have geared ourselves to an overall planning program capability. This means that we do not wait until the military decides it wants a specific kind of weapon, or a particular system. We want to come in at the stage when the military has a problem and is seeking its solution. The well-grounded defense contractor must be prepared to help on the problem level, then to take the project all the way from problem to actual hardware."

This is a new kind of philosophy in industrial management. It complements the philosophy of concurrency that gave the U.S.

Air Force their mightiest strategic weapons on an "impossible" time-schedule. It also suggests an answer to the closing question of Chapter Four: "What are the odds in favor of free enterprise?"

6.

From DAYS of the VIKINGS

"Our aim is an easy one to describe. It is to concentrate the full breadth and depth of our technical and managerial skills on the effort to achieve the highest standards of overall performance. Anything less will be unsatisfactory."

— *William B. Bergen, President, Martin Company*

TITAN, the Free World's mightiest single deterrent to war, is more than a missile. It is even more than its future promise as a heavyweight launch vehicle for peaceful scientific research in space. It is a personification of one aspect of American folklore, the success story. In this sense it is a classical symbol of the vitality, creativity and honesty inherent in the free enterprise system. It represents the dynamic comeback of a great pioneering aircraft company. It contains within its monumental frame the story of a group of talented, boldly imaginative scientists and engineers who, when they most needed him, found a strong executive leader with honest faith in them.

The TITAN ICBM encompasses a history of progressions in both scientific research at new frontiers and national defense. Its family tree is firmly rooted in an early "Norseman" of the upper atmosphere, the VIKING research rocket—first big space vehicle of original American design. A sturdy branch on that tree is MATADOR, "The Killer" cruise missile—first operational weapon system in the United States. An even sturdier branch is VANGUARD, the "rocket engineer's rocket," which has con-

159

tributed more to the art of American rocketry than any other design of the past or present. TITAN also encompasses the growth of a leading member of the aerospace industry through a series of dramatic name-changes: from the Glenn L. Martin Company, to The Martin Company, to Martin Company Division of the Martin Marietta Corporation.

History usually moves in ponderous ways, yet the Martin transition from the production of airplanes to missiles and scientific space research took little more than a dozen years. The reason behind this explosive development was implied by Bastian "Buzz" Hello, veteran aeronautical engineer at the company. "I remember when I first came here," he told me. "All of us junior engineers were required to take a training course. The engineer who taught the course started us off by talking about the feasibility of artificial Earth satellites. That was in 1948. His name was Bill Bergen. He's now President of the Martin Company Division."

In 1948, only the most visionary among engineers thought about man-made satellites as a practical possibility. Only the most daring of them openly discussed that possibility. At the time, the major big rocket booster being used experimentally in the United States was the German V-2, of which a limited number had been captured.

During that same period, nevertheless, the Glenn L. Martin Company engineers were hard-bent on a task with the Naval Research Laboratory to design and produce a rocket for the exploration and analysis of the upper atmosphere. Little was known in those days about the specific composition and electronic, as well as nuclear, reactions of the ionosphere. Except for tentative data gathered by the not always successful launches of the V-2 and Bumper (a combination of the V-2 with a small WAC-Corporal second stage), most of man's knowledge of the topmost atmospheric layers was educated guesswork. Balloon probes of the stratosphere, which is much closer to Earth than the ionosphere, supplied additional valuable but restricted information. Yet if man was ever to soar through outer space, if he was ever to understand (and perhaps someday to control) the vagaries of weather conditions on his planet, he first needed precise knowledge of those fierce natural forces ceaselessly in conflict above the stratosphere. Such knowledge was also vital to national security, in terms of the development of ultrareliable communications systems and navigational instruments. The first Martin VIKING was launched in collaboration with the Navy at the Army's White Sands Proving Ground on May 3, 1949. It reached a speed of 2,250 miles an hour and climbed 51½ miles. Both its speed and altitude had been previously far exceeded by a Bumper-Project WAC-Corporal. The difference was that VIKING carried a payload of 464 pounds of special instruments to measure upper-air pressure and temperature. This was at least nine times the payload of the little WAC-Corporal. However, it was but a fourth the payload capability of the V-2 for approximately the same altitude. But the VIKING's rocket engine developed only about a third the thrust of that in the V-2. So it was a good competitive start for America.

The next two VIKINGS didn't do as well as the first. Respectively, they reached 32 and 50 miles of altitude. VIKING Number Four made history. It shot away from the Earth to 106.4 miles, a record for single-stage rockets. The flight made possible the measurement of cosmic-ray intensities above the Equator, another "first." There was also a "second," since this VIKING was the second big rocket ever to be launched from a ship at sea. A V-2 had earlier been launched by the Navy from the aircraft carrier *Midway* off the Bermudas. The VIKING flight, launched under difficult conditions from the deck of the USS *Norton Sound* in Pacific equatorial waters, showed the way toward the feasibility of future submarine-launched POLARIS missiles.

With one exception (VIKING Number Eight) that was destroyed during a captive firing of its engine at White Sands, the VIKING lineage developed nobly. As the Martin engineers gained experience from each flight, they modified the succeeding research rocket for better performance. VIKING Number

Seven rose 136 miles into the ionosphere at 4,100 miles an hour, breaking its VIKING Number Four's record by 30 miles of altitude. VIKING Number Ten equalled this new record on May 7, 1954. Eighteen days later, VIKING Number Eleven exceeded all others by soaring 158 miles into the sky at an ultimate speed of 4,300 mph. Number Twelve was the last of the VIKINGS, as such. It reached 154 miles altitude.

On October 7, 1955, forty days after the United States officially proclaimed that we would launch instrumented man-made satellites as a scientific contribution to the International Geophysical Year, The Martin Company was awarded the prime contract for Project VANGUARD. The Project was under the supervision of the Naval Research Laboratory. Thus maintained was the highly successful military-industrial teamwork that made VIKING possible. Two additional VIKINGS were diverted to the VANGUARD program as test vehicles.

In fact, the VIKING research rocket program had laid the physical foundation upon which a satellite-launch and instrument program must stand to be successful. The launching of eleven VIKINGS, excluding the single failure, from 1949 through 1954 had taught scientists at the Naval Research Laboratory how to design and build recording instruments that were not only lightweight, compact and precise but were also capable of enduring the roughest kind of treatment that could be encountered in a rocket flight. Those same launchings taught Martin engineers how to design and build the most aerodynamically efficient and rugged structures in rocketry of that period. The 20,000-pound-thrust VIKING, long before its flight-test series was ended, had superbly outperformed the V-2 with a 60,000-pound-thrust engine.

Among the many unique instruments designed and built for VIKING to probe the upper atmosphere were: a tough automatic camera that would not break up as it impacted with the ground and yet took the sharpest photographs from ultrahigh altitudes at that time; "bottles" that scooped actual samples of ions (electrically charged atoms) out of the ionosphere; pressure-sensing devices and counters for cosmic, ultraviolet, X- and other kinds of solar rays. Flights of the VIKINGS also contributed much to an understanding of the phenomenon of friction heating caused by air molecules rubbing against metals at high speeds.

INTERESTING SIDELIGHTS

Some interesting sidelights were described to me by William G. Purdy, the Martin engineer who was in charge of the VIKING development. Purdy was just 30 years old when he was assigned one of the most challenging jobs in the aircraft industry. From 1947 to mid-1954 he and those who worked with him met that challenge, often by sheer ingenuity. He is a lanky, friendly individual, who today still wears a crewcut along with his bifocals.

"The matter of determining the size of VIKING," he told me, "was restricted by the widest piece of standard rolled aluminum sheet we could find. That gave us a diameter of 32 inches." In other words, the "mighty" VIKING research rocket had to be engineered to fit the inadequate materials available in that period.

Again, to quote Purdy: "You needed lots of skills—but one of the things you needed most was resourcefulness. For example, with VIKING Number Ten we had an explosion in the engine compartment during a captive firing. The explosion played hell with the compartment but didn't completely demolish it. The rocket just sat on the stand and burned. In the process, it put the electrical system out of commission. The fuel and oxidizer tanks are equipped with vent valves. If you want to unload the fuel or oxidizer, you have to open the valves to let air in. Otherwise the tanks would collapse from change in pressure. Well, we couldn't get to the rocket to open the valves and alcohol from the fuel tank was slowly dribbling out of a small line at its bottom. We certainly wanted to save what remained of VIKING Ten because on VIKING we saved everything we could and used it over again. So here we saw the prospect of the whole thing collapsing before our eyes. It was not a pleasant prospect. But our Navy program officer, a Lieutenant Pitts, saved the day. He snatched a carbine from the guard inside the door of the blockhouse and dashed outside and shot a hole through the alcohol tank. The hole was enough to vent the tank and we saved the rocket. We took it back to Baltimore, repaired it, returned it to White Sands and fired it up to 136 miles."

Purdy, like every engineer in the rocket business, often uses the phrase "state of the art." He explained that to me. "We're generally used to dealing with equipment that has a high state of reliability—washing machines, automobiles, telephones, bridges, almost anything you might care to mention. The reason for this high reliability is that the evolution of the design of these machines and devices has extended over a very long period of time.

"For example: the automobile, over the course of a large number of decades, has been service-tested by almost countless people. The new model that comes out annually is not much different from the past models. Sure, it's different in its chrome-work and different in body style—but it's not different essentially. Basic changes are made very slowly in the things we normally deal with, things that pertain to our normal daily lives. There's an awful lot of proof that these things are good the way they are basically, through an awful lot of testing by an awful lot of people.

"In the missile business it isn't possible to settle down on firm hardware that you know would be reliable. We can't wait those 25 or 30 years to prove that the hardware is reliable. In the past, at least, it has been necessary to force the state of the art in order to get a set of hardware that meets the stringent requirements established by the military, or by NASA, or the user, whoever he might be. This simply means that it's been fundamental to the missile business to start off with unreliable hardware —because it is an assemblage of hardware for which, generally, there is no really extended precedent."

Bill Purdy, as of this writing, is General Manager of TITAN

III at the Denver subdivision of Martin Marietta's Martin Company Division. For the company, he's engineering boss of the TITAN program. His self-critical attitude about reliability has helped considerably to make TITAN the most reliable liquid-fuel ICBM in the SAC inventory. His philosophy is expressed as follows: "We're about at the point where our technical experience—and our state-of-the-art foundation, if you will—is sufficiently broad to allow us a return to the classical engineering approach. That is, as long as you can make your machine work well, build it as darned strong and as darned dependable as you can. Forget about whether its design is optimum. So what if it's a little heavy? What if it may last three times as long as it's required to last? At least you'll be certain of its undisputable reliability."

Some missile engineers might consider Purdy's attitude quite controversial. The tradition in rocketry, brief as it is, has been to design a system for optimum use, and no further. Which is to say that a missile design should meet military requirements as favorably as possible without going a shade beyond those requirements. Yet often in the past, military missiles have had to be modified beyond such requirements for important space research, both military and civilian. "Optimum" in missilery is a sliding scale, depending upon the mission. Purdy favors an unconventional type of missile engineering, the kind that permits the missile to be easily adaptable with equal reliability to a number of missions, some of them perhaps unforeseen.

COMPETITIVE IDEAS, UNORTHODOX APPROACHES

In a monolithic political society like that of Russia, where competitive ideas and unorthodox approaches to problems are not tolerated, men of Purdy's strong convictions might very well be liquidated or summarily toppled from leading positions. In the free-enterprise system, however, Purdy steadily advanced to positions of ever-increasing responsibility as he made original contributions to his company.

Yet Bill Purdy is only one among a number of strongly motivated and outspoken engineers that made up the original hardcore group at the Glenn L. Martin Company and led it to a pinnacle of scientific achievement. One of the most forward-looking members of that group was George S. Trimble, Jr., now Vice President in charge of Advanced Programs.

Trimble is an amiable, rather slim, balding man of about the same age as Purdy. He has a lively interest in science as well as engineering. Intensely dedicated to maintaining the security of the Free World, he is also highly enthusiastic about the beneficial possibilities of peaceful space research. He feels strongly that anything the human mind is capable of conceiving can be engineered into reality. I once asked him whether he thought it would ever be possible to broadcast electrical power by radio from a satellite producing electricity through conversion of sunlight in space. Orbital power stations of this sort, if ever achieved, could not only tremendously reduce the cost of electricity production but could also focus that power to any selected area of the Earth, no matter how inaccessible the area may seem today. The idea would appear fantastic, even utterly impossible, to most engineers. Trimble's matter-of-fact answer was: "It should certainly be possible to broadcast electrical power. We don't know how to do it now, but we'll find out!"

He made that statement to me in 1955, shortly after his company had been awarded the Project VANGUARD contract—two full years before the first sputnik was launched into orbit.

Also during 1955, Trimble was one of several Martin executives responsible for the establishment of a unique concept among profit-making organizations. This was the founding and financing of a completely independent nonprofit institution for the pursuit of pure scientific research. It was called the Research Institute for Advanced Studies. Leading scientists and mathematicians from all over the world were invited and subsidized for varying periods as residents of the Institute to work on the most profound problems of physics, chemistry and mathematics. Among the problems were Einstein's Unsymmetrical

Field Theory (left unsolved by his death), the basic nature of gravity, the mechanism by which green plants transmute light energy and carbon dioxide gas into protein-rich food, sugar and oxygen and a mathematical clarification of nonlinear dynamics. There was also a staff of foremost scientists permanently in residence to pursue the solution of these problems—any one of which, if solved, would revolutionize all of science. The Martin Company provided funds and equipment—high-speed electronic computers, electron and ion microscopes, precision optical and test instruments—and rented a cluster of buildings surrounded and isolated by acres of woodland in the rolling hills outside Baltimore. The idea was to give the scientists and mathematicians both seclusion and security—necessary requirements for the solution of profound natural mysteries. No demands were imposed on them. No strings were attached. No profit was expected. They were entirely free to publish papers on their discoveries in scientific journals. The Research Institute for Advanced Studies, RIAS for short, was closer in concept to scientific institutes supported by major universities and foundations than to anything heretofore established by a private industrial firm.

In a real sense, RIAS expresses the visionary approach of the Martin engineering management. For George Trimble, William B. Bergen and Welcome W. Bender, among others, early recognized that an investment in pure scientific research was an investment in the future, even as General of the Air Force "Hap" Arnold understood a decade before that science was the key to Free World security. In probing the mysteries of Nature for no other reason than pure curiosity, unexpected discoveries could thoroughly transform the state of modern technology.

Welcome Bender was the first Director of RIAS. Under his astute and enthusiastic management the Institute has become one of the world's important scientific institutions. Today, Bender is Director of Research for the total Martin Company Division of Martin Marietta Corporation. But he has not relinquished his immediate directorship of RIAS, which he continues simultaneously to manage on the rigorous basis of its original concept: the pursuit of fundamental scientific knowledge with no commercial interference.

Bender, as Bergen and Trimble, has spanned two eras of flight in his career with the company. He started as a designer of aircraft and electronic components in 1939 and now has overall responsibility for the programming, integration and quality of space research. His transition began with the Killer, the Martin-Matador missile of the Air Force. In 1945, he was appointed Technical Director of the company's Pilotless Aircraft Program. The time was coincidental with the completion of Dr. Theodore van Kármán's first report to General Arnold on the feasibility of both winged and ballistic missiles. Bender's research led directly to a development contract for the B-61 Matador, a pilotless bomber that electronically guided itself to the target. The B-61 was the first American cruise missile to achieve actual production status. Its initial full-range flight was made on June 20, 1951, from Cape Canaveral to the Bahamas. The Air Force Missile Test Center at Cape Canaveral had been formally established only a month and a week earlier. Shorter-range test flights of the B-61 had been made at Holloman Air Force Base, New Mexico, starting in December 1950. It was at Holloman that Colonel "Red" Wetzel received his assignment as Air Force Project Officer on the B-61 Matador program. This was his first experience with a missile weapon system, as it was also for the Glenn L. Martin Company.

REVOLUTIONARY WEAPON CONCEPT

In fact, the Matador provided the primary successful proof that the Air Force weapon-system concept was valid and necessary. The system concept was later applied to the design of aircraft as well as of missiles. Previously, fighter aircraft and bombers were designed as individual airplanes, without much more thought than the purpose of their missions. Through a series of flight tests, required modifications were gradually revealed in terms of pilot efficiency, maintenance and support equipment. This was not only costly—an entire cockpit, including instruments and controls, might have to be redesigned —but wasteful of time and skilled energy. With the weapon-system approach, all aspects of a combat instrument are conceived in advance, including the human limitations of a pilot, launch director or maintenance crew. By official definition of the United States Air Force: "The complete weapon system includes all related facilities, equipment, materiel, services and personnel required solely for the operation of the aerospace vehicle . . . so that the instrument of combat becomes a self-sufficient unit of striking power in its intended operational environment."

On these terms, the Martin-Matador pioneered a revolutionary engineering approach to the defense of the Free World. At the time, the very designation of Matador—B-61—reflected the conventional thinking of even the youngest and therefore, by implication, the most vitally unconventional of the military departments. The "B" stood for "bomber," pilotless or not. Since then, the Matador has been redesignated as "TM-61," for "Tactical Missile." Its second-generation relatives, the TM-76A and B, the Mace, can travel almost three times as far within the same range of speed and altitude. Both tactical cruise missiles can fly over the treetops or soar above 40,000 feet; both have a speed just below the supersonic; both can transport conventional high-explosive or nuclear warheads. The Mace "B Model" is sent on its way from a hardened launcher of reinforced concrete and steel. Despite the fact that the Matador and Mace are rather undramatic by today's standards, they still effectively support the tactical deterrent strength of democracy by deployment in West Germany, Okinawa, Korea and Taiwan (Formosa).

Perhaps more importantly, the Matador forced the Glenn L. Martin Company into the field of electronics in an advanced manner. Because of the requirements of the weapon-system concept, Martin as prime contractor on the Matador had to diversify its research and development proclivities. The company had to conceive of the entire missile system as an integrated whole, which included electronic guidance, a mobile launcher and a rocket engine to boost the Matador on its way from the point of zero-launch. Experience acquired in the rocket-boosting of a Matador from a standing start to jet-flight speed also helped the Air Force to develop a zero-launcher for the manned F-84 fighter-bomber. The F-84, which played an important role early in the Korean War, was a product of Republic Aviation—a company competitive with Martin. Yet the Air Force was able to apply the genius of one industrial organization to that of another and thus arrive at a new technique in weaponry. Such is the healthy "fallout" or bonus that can only be derived from a free-enterprise society.

This kind of fallout, of course, is also exceedingly beneficial to each company. A prime contractor has to study with care every minute aspect of the system over which he has final authority and responsibility. Otherwise he would be unable to evaluate the skills and tooling needed by subcontractors for the efficient production of system components. The word "efficient" here encompasses not only precision and minimum cost but also the rigorous meeting of time schedules. One subcontractor, producing, say, a small relay or automatic electrical switch, could delay an urgent program, because of poor design, production or delivery. The delay would be recorded by the military as a mark against the prime contractor, since it is his management responsibility to produce the total system on schedule. The mark would also weigh negatively on his record in a Government evaluation of any future proposals by that contractor. For this reason, aerospace contractors choose and monitor their subcontractors with more than average attention. In the process, they gain ever-increasing specialized experience that can be applied to other systems.

Diversification and versatility are keynotes of free-enterprise industry, especially of the aerospace industry. During the late 1940's and the early 1950's, the Glenn L. Martin Company was simultaneously engaged in programs as varied as the VIKING research rocket, the Matador cruise missile, the XB-51 (an Air Force experimental manned bomber with three turbojet engines), the XP4M-1 (a Navy experimental piloted bomber with four engines, two of them jet and two conventional), the redesign and production of the British Canberra twin-jet light bomber for Air Force use in the Korean War and a thirty-six passenger twin-engine luxury airliner, the famous Martin 2-0-2. The latter, in a follow-up pressurized version, was known as the 4-0-4. A number of these airliners are still in use today. They were good airplanes, but they almost caused the company's financial collapse.

The Glenn L. Martin Company, during World War II, had been thoroughly geared to supply military needs, the production of Army bombers and Navy flying boats. The postwar field of commercial aircraft production was highly competitive. It demanded extensive retooling and a new way of thinking. But the company had, a decade earlier, designed and built one of the most renowned commercial airplanes of its day—the all-metal monoplane flying boat called the China Clipper, which carried 46 passengers and a crew of five. Besides, the company was America's oldest manufacturer of aircraft. Old Glenn L. Martin himself didn't have the slightest doubt that aviation was here to stay and that he could produce commercial airplanes at a profit. The coming age of rocketry and spaceflight was not quite as bright on his horizon as it was before the eyes of the younger engineers who designed his products. Actually, in favor of commercial aircraft he withdrew from an opportunity to obtain a huge Air Force contract for new jet bombers. Instead, the company obtained heavy bank-financing for the airliner venture.

MANAGEMENT ENGINEERING LEADERSHIP

But the genius and strong convictions of young aeronautical engineers are not the kind of adhesive that alone can hold a large company intact. Executive managerial leadership of the same calibre is also required. At one dark point toward the end of the Matador test program, the company began to fall apart financially. It was en route to bankruptcy because it could not compete in the open market with the leading producers of commercial aircraft. The tightly knit Martin team of imaginative engineers was threatened with dissolution, to be scattered among the other companies. Such teams are not developed in a day, a year, or even in a decade. They form their peculiarly intimate professional interrelationships by sweating through almost numberless big and little problems.

Their worth as a working group cannot be measured by money or individual skills. If they are scattered by the winds of poor financial management, the nation is the loser. For the health and progress of a free society depends upon competition. And the achievement of higher quality industrial or scientific products for defense depends upon avid competition between well-knit teams of engineers or scientists.

Such teams are the true wealth of any one company or laboratory. Yet they cannot be expected to establish financial policies. They have their own important jobs to accomplish in other fields. A man may have explicit experience in organizing the production techniques of a diamond mine—without being able to sell diamonds.

The Mellon National National Bank of Pittsburgh, Pa., as well as the Government's Reconstruction Finance Corporation, both heavy investors, recognized this and acted to save the Glenn L. Martin Company from disaster. They called in George M. Bunker, a management engineer who had had considerable experience in correcting serious financial problems of industry. He was President of the Trailmobile Company, second largest manufacturer of truck-trailers in America, when he agreed to take on the failing Glenn L. Martin Company.

George Bunker is a modest man with a rare background. Now in his early fifties, he was barely past forty when he sat down in the Martin driver's seat—a young man commanding the nation's oldest corporation in its field. At first glance he may not have seemed the likely type to succeed—at least to many executives of the company. As he told me: "I am not an aeronautical engineer. Actually, I'm a chemical engineer. But in that sense, I haven't practiced for a good many years." He has about him an easygoing air of kindliness—again, at least outwardly, a quality not often considered conducive to the ruthless reorganization of a giant corporation. But this is only because the popular image of great industrial leaders is misleading and distorted. In his easy way, George Bunker allows little to fluster him. He evaluates problems calmly and expects a certain proportion of failure to be integral with success. He also expects men to act like human beings, with their proportion of emotion, stubbornness and even self-righteousness sometimes blinding their intelligence, experience and good judgment. His method is to give men the full opportunity to face these all-too-human shortcomings, which most of us easily recognize in others but refuse to admit in ourselves. He feels that when individuals are placed in situations about which they are critical, they tend to understand the other fellow's problems with sympathy and to admit their own original shortcomings in the matter. An intuitive brilliance of Bunker's is that he knows when men need leadership for emotional security and when they need a friendly cooperative ear for discussion on an equal level to develop or establish the validity of their ideas.

Of medium build, neatly conservative in dress, positive in his speech and with alert brown eyes emphasized by dark heavy brows and black-framed glasses, George M. Bunker could be mistaken for a career diplomat or president of a university. He graduated from Massachusetts Institute of Technology in 1931 —"Which wasn't a very good year," as he puts it. His first job was in a Chicago factory of the Campbell Soup Company. After several years, he managed to obtain employment in the Industrial Engineering Department of Wilson & Company, well-known meat-packers. "I stayed there until I could get out— which was a couple of years," he told me. His next job was really a turning point in his career. It was with the management engineering firm of A. T. Kearney & Company, also in Chicago. The Company was management consultant to a variety of industrial firms. Within a half-dozen years, George Bunker was made a partner of A. T. Kearney.

"Everything I learned about business-management, I learned there," he said. "It was the beginning of my combining a background in engineering with management experience. I learned not only by the very nature of my work at Kearney, but also by watching at firsthand how a great many diverse managements operate. I had this great advantage: I saw a lot of industrial scenery over a relatively short number of years."

Next, Bunker went to the Kroger Company in Cincinnati, Ohio, as Vice President in charge of Manufacturing. This was a focal point for all his past experience in engineering, management and the production of food. It was also, to quote him, "by far the largest operation I had ever come up against until I arrived at Martin." He had nearly 7,000 people to manage at Kroger, since that company manufactures their own private-label products, which make up the biggest part of goods sold nationally through their stores.

Bunker's final move before arriving at Martin was, of course, the Trailmobile Company, where an extremely serious financial situation had forced a change in the management. He was asked to take over as President. While nursing the company back to health, he acquired additional experience with a heavier type of industry, rounding out his background as a unique manager for the Glenn L. Martin Company.

CONFIDENCE AS POSITIVE ACTION

His first positive action after arriving in Baltimore was to establish a firm feeling of confidence in the Company's durability. The year was 1952. "In those days," he informed me, "the Company did have some very serious financial problems. One of the great worries was that we might lose an important part of our technical capability, simply because people might think they were working for an unstable company. This was one of the reasons that led to a change of management.

"It was obvious (there was no question about it) that the area in which we were losing money was commercial aircraft. The first thing we did, of course, was at once to abandon the idea of making and selling more commercial aircraft. In this way, we could concentrate on other programs that were then in the house. The Korean War was with us. There were orders on the books to be filled. We just came in early and worked late."

George Bunker's modesty is evident in the way he consistently uses the pronoun "we." Rarely does he ever say "I" when he talks about the re-formation of a company that is today the producer of a greater variety of missile weapon systems than any other. It has also become, under his leadership, probably the most diversified organization in the fields of science and technology of the whole of American industry. This naturally includes the far-ranging facilities of American-Marietta Company for metallurgical, chemical and construction materials research as well as production. George Bunker was mainly responsible for the Martin-Marietta merger, which provided an even healthier financial base for the two companies and even greater prospects for scientific as well as technological advancement. Up to the time of the merger, Bunker was Chairman of the Board of Directors at Martin. After the merger, he was elected President and Chief Executive Officer—in other words, the active manager—of the new corporation. Yet he assumes no individual credit for his leadership.

His attitude is: "The fact that the previous Martin management was no longer in command, the management that had put the company into the commercial aircraft business so extensively, seemed in itself almost at once to be a reassurance to the personnel. Adequate financing had been arranged. It appeared that the company would be likely to survive if we managed it well."

No important changes were made in engineering management at Martin. The hard-core group of visionary engineers maintained their authority as technical managers. Bunker, in fact, did everything he could to help them feel ever more secure. "I like to think," he said, "that my presence had an advantage. Here was someone who had come from outside the industry, someone who, if I may say so, wasn't really job-hunting at the time and yet was willing to throw in his lot with these people who had been caught in an unfortunate set of circumstances; this must have had a beneficial psychological effect."

The beneficial psychological effect certainly extended beyond the simple presence of George Bunker. It derived from the basic honesty of the man himself. He expressed his credo to me in these words: "Whoever has the ultimate responsibility for decisions must be willing not only to take the praise and the rewards for a success but also to take the lumps that come with failure. This, I personally think, is of substantial importance. In a business such as ours, you have your share of failures."

"But isn't it true," I asked, "that often the 'failures' are more apparent than real?"

He nodded. "To some degree on every project we are endeavoring to do something that has never been done before. If it had been done, there would be no purpose to any research project."

"Wasn't that particularly true of Project VANGUARD? Most people among the press and public at the time considered it almost a complete failure. Many probably still do today."

Bunker answered me with firm conviction. "The VANGUARD as a matter of practical fact was one of the most successful rocket programs ever conceived and executed. And you will find a host of knowledgeable scientific and technical people who will back up that statement! Every successful rocket or missile today owes a part of its heritage to the VANGUARD Program."

Substantiating his statement is an unclassified footnote in a security-classified engineering report. "The VANGUARD vehicle is considered 'operational' inasmuch as a thorough analysis of the TV-4BU flight was the first such effort on VANGUARD that resulted in no significant vehicle change recommendations. It is considered a major engineering achievement to have developed an 'operational' multistage space vehicle after a program of 14 flight firings."

TV-4BU stands for "Test Vehicle, Number Four Back-up." It was launched on September 18, 1959 and placed 137 pounds into orbit with an accuracy error of only five-hundredths of a degree. This is equivalent to hitting a bullseye several hundreds of miles up in the sky that is exactly ten times smaller than the apparent diameter of the full moon.

Yet on September 6, 1959, while TV-4BU was being prepared for its flight at Cape Canaveral, the Louisville *Courier-Journal* felt justified in headlining a wire-service story as follows: "LAST OF THE HARD-LUCK VANGUARDS TO BE FIRED WITHIN NEXT TEN DAYS." The press and public image of VANGUARD was hardly complimentary to The Martin Company, the Naval Research Laboratory and, later, the National Aeronautics and Space Administration. Straightening out the public record is long past due.

A MONUMENT TO INGENUITY

Project VANGUARD endures as a monument to the ingenuity and craftsmanship of a free-enterprise society. It was conceived as a low-priority, low-cost program. Originally its established goal was to launch successfully at least one satellite in six attempts. This was stretched later to eleven attempts, since five rockets of the series that had been intended purely for flight-testing with simulated payloads were added to the actual satellite-launch program. Altogether, fourteen rockets made up the test and launch series. The first two were modified VIKINGS, used to develop staging techniques. The VANGUARD was a three-stage rocket, uniquely combining all types of propulsion systems available at that time. The first-stage engine used liquid cryogenic propellants—kerosene and supercold liquid oxygen. The second-stage engine was propelled by liquid hypergolics—white fuming nitric acid and unsymmetrical dimethyl hydrazine. These were storable at normal temperatures and required no igniting device, since they ignite upon contact with each other. The third stage had a solid-fuel rocket engine. This was long before the superficial but intense controversy over liquid versus solid-fuel rockets. Within the VANGUARD design, both kinds played important roles determined by their advantages. VANGUARD was also a finless rocket, a startling innovation then.

VANGUARD outdid its established goals by boosting three satellites into orbit with amazing accuracy. But its major contributions to rocketry went far beyond the program. Examples of this fallout are almost numberless. The most spectacular probably was the highly successful launching of Telstar I, the first orbital electronic station in space to relay live commercial television programs between Europe and North America. The Telstar was launched by a three-stage rocket, the last two stages of which were copied from the last two VANGUARD stages. This was almost 3 full years after the final VANGUARD was launched. VANGUARD also pioneered solid-fuel stages now used in the MINUTEMAN ICBM and the POLARIS submarine-launched strategic missile. VANGUARD second and third stages are also incorporated into a variety of dependable space-research workhorse launch vehicles, such as the THOR-ABLE, THOR-ABLE-STAR, THOR-DELTA, ATLAS-ABLE and SCOUT.

Why, then, was VANGUARD dubbed a "hard luck rocket" and a failure by the press and public? Mainly because of the Russian sputnik launches. Public pride was perhaps hurt that the Russians had placed their satellites in orbit first. VANGUARD stood as a symbol of hope to regain lost prestige. It was our only satellite-launch vehicle at the time. Even then it did not launch the first American satellite. This was accomplished by a modified military missile, the JUPITER, which enjoyed a much higher priority in its development than the nonmilitary VANGUARD. Then a series of seeming failures, inherent in any rocket development program, made it appear to the technically uninformed that VANGUARD was a sorry mess and a waste of money.

From VANGUARD, however, came the basic engineering plan for the Free World's most powerful ICBM. Outwardly, on a grander scale, the TITAN ICBM even resembles the bullet-shaped VANGUARD. It, too, is finless and staged. More than this, out of the VANGUARD came a close cooperative team effort between two great members of the aerospace industry— Martin Marietta Corporation and the Aerojet-General Corporation. Aerojet had developed the VANGUARD second-stage engine to Martin specifications. From this experience, Aerojet went on easily to the mightier engines for both stages of TITANS I and II. The latter uses the same storable liquid fuel of VANGUARD, if not the same oxidizer. Because of this, TITAN II can be stored fully fueled in an underground silo, ready to be launched almost instantly from below the surface of the Earth if this tragically should ever prove to be necessary.

Apart from Project VANGUARD's vital contributions to national security, in the realm of public pride it was hardly an effort to inspire shame among Americans. The first VAN-GUARD satellite, launched (ahead of schedule) about 6 months after the first Russian sputnik was fired into orbit, is still transmitting radio signals. It is the world's oldest active satellite in space. Today, some rocket engineers talk half-facetiously about shooting it down before it becomes a real space traffic problem and interferes with more modern satellite communications. Sputnik I went silent in three weeks and fell out of orbit 3 months after it was launched.

Elaborating on and illuminating the incredible engineering genius that could perfect VANGUARD in only fourteen test-firings, it need only be said that the German V-2 required more than 2,500 flight tests before it became operational. And VANGUARD was many times more original in concept than the V-2.

Of course, VANGUARD did have an advantage: Martin engineers had acquired preliminary experience with the VI-KING research rocket. But it, as well, was much more advanced than the V-2. Their experience encompassed eleven test-firings.

Again, we have a graphic example of free-enterprise ingenuity, the superiority of a system that encourages competition in a free-ranging manner. The Nazis, like the Communists, could concentrate larger amounts of money and manpower on a particular project than can the biggest corporations of the Free World; effort of such scope, however, represents a centralized approach to a military or political goal. The individual has very limited freedom of action within the confines of that goal. He is not stimulated to experiment far from the safety of well-worn paths, since he is commanded, either by implication or proclamation, to produce. Obversely, in a free society people are *asked* to produce for their own profit, whether this be money, personal satisfaction, or dedicated patriotism.

The VIKING was responsible for the world's first gimbaled rocket engines. Automatic electronic and pressure controls cause the whole engine to swing one way or another so that the exhaust-thrust can steer the rocket and stabilize its flight when necessary. The gimbal concept made finless rockets feasible. The German V-2 as well as early big American missiles used carbon vanes for stability and steering. These were placed around the engine to deflect its exhaust by moving one vane or another, much as the rudder, elevators and ailerons control the direction and stability of an airplane. As with the airplane also, fixed surfaces—vertical and horizontal stabilizers—were required. These were the fins. Their value in maintaining a rocket's stability was offset by the air resistance that resulted during the initial period of flight, which in terms of acceleration and accuracy is the most important period for a missile. The big liquid-fuel strategic missiles of today all use gimbaled engines.

GIANT CONTRIBUTIONS FROM A "PYGMY"

Despite the giant contributions to rocketry made by the VIKING, by today's standards it was rather a pygmy in physical size. It is thoroughly dwarfed by its descendant, the eleven-story TITAN. A vivid illustration of the rapid progress made in rocketry within less than a dozen years was an educational film released by the Glenn L. Martin Company near the end of the VIKING Program. One scene shows a VIKING strapped onto a large dolly being pushed toward a railroad siding at the Baltimore plant. Three men are maneuvering the rocket as the commentator states in dramatic tones that "the mighty rocket is transported on flat cars to the White Sands Proving Ground in New Mexico." Another scene shifts to the Proving Ground, where a small crew of men is manually rolling the "giant" gantry servicing tower to the launch-pad. It moves along on wheels. At Cape Canaveral, the TITAN servicing towers have no wheels. They cannot be budged by the shoulders of an army. Each of them weighs 150 tons. They are called CMEs, or Complete Missile Erectors, and are fully automatic. They are lowered to receive the first stage of a true brute of a missile and lift it into place on the pad, then again are lowered to receive and raise the second stage. The raising or lowering process takes a mere 5 minutes. Within their heavy steel framework are sets of elevators to transport members of the servicing crew from base-level to the platforms that surround the missile at various dizzying heights. The basic design of those platforms, which fold outwardly away from the missile prior to lowering the CME for launch, was developed from experience with the VANGUARD servicing tower.

The VANGUARD Program began at Martin 3 years after the arrival there of George M. Bunker. While he was en route to his seeing a great aerospace organization through its period of growing pains, the company name had been changed to The Martin Company. Almost simultaneously with the Navy award of Project VANGUARD's prime contract to The Martin Company, George Bunker had to make one of the most difficult decisions of his career. This was whether or not to invest the company resources, including valuable skilled man-hours, in the development of a sound engineering proposal for the TITAN ICBM, which then had a nameless designation, WS-107A-2. The Air Force had included The Martin Company on one of its invitational proposal lists for the new long-range weapon system. Yet, superficially, the ranking competitors for the contract stood a better chance than Martin. They had worked more closely and much longer with the Air Force on rockets. Martin's work in rocketry had been mainly with the Naval Research Laboratory.

In a freely competitive society, profit is required for a company to survive. The Martin Company had been teetering financially over the abyss of disaster. It was an acute situation for Bunker to face.

He expressed the situation like this: "The first and most important step was to try and evaluate what Martin's chances might be—and then to authorize the proposal. The other contractors at that point had a leg up on us. Certainly Lockheed did.

"One of the big problems in the management of a company such as ours is to decide where you are going to expend your most precious asset—your technical capability. Wasting the time of our conceptual people on an unsuccessful proposal would be an absolutely total loss. And I mean a loss that transcends the cost of the proposal—not that we don't watch costs carefully too. But we are much more unhappy if we fail to put all that talent on an alternate route that might secure for us a definite contract.

"This was a fairly critical decision to make. But there was no doubt in my mind that we were dealing with a program of the highest priority. There was no doubt in my mind that the successful contractor would be taking on not only a very large program, but a very important one.

"So I made the final decision affirmatively. Without any question, the incentive to make that decision came from our people who had been watching the whole thing closely and who felt they *could* win."

Among those people were Bill Bergen, George Trimble and Bill Purdy. Bunker, himself an engineer, could see that they *knew* what they were telling him.

"We really did *have* the technological capability," he told me. "But as a matter of fact, I think that the selection of Martin by the Air Force Source Selection Board came as something of a surprise to some of the people in the Ballistic Missile Division, or the Western Development Division, as it was called then. I think that they rather felt one of the other contractors would be accepted."

The award of contract WS-107A-2 to The Martin Company certainly indicates that the Air Force plays no favorites with civilian industry. They try always to buy the highest quality at the lowest reasonable cost. Again quoting Dr. Alfred Rockefeller, Jr., historian for the Air Force ballistic missile programs, The Martin Company "made a very interesting proposal. They recognized that this country at the time had no integrated ballistic missile facilities per se. They declared that, if given the contract, they were going to design and build at their own expense a totally integrated production plant in the middle of the country. The plant would not only manufacture the missiles but would check them out through all phases and fire them under flight-simulated conditions in captive test stands."

A TRUCKLOAD OF EXPERIENCE

That was an important and original aspect of the Martin proposal. Even more important was the group of men who compiled the proposal, which, as George Bunker describes it, "looked like a truckload of volumes, with all the copies involved." Regarding those men, Bunker adds: "We simply had more practical design and operating experience on liquid-fuel rockets than did anybody else. Despite its size, the proposal didn't take a great deal of time. The factor here is that engineering proposals don't consume a great deal of time if you have a solid background in the matter about which you are asked to propose an approach. But if you have to develop your philosophy, then organize an engineering team and then study a variety of alternate approaches to assure that you have the right solution to the problem, you of course consume much more time. But we were ready in advance."

Regardless of the readiness, a good many fingers were crossed by Martin engineering personnel. According to Bill Purdy: "There's a great deal of superstition in the rocket business. Some of us still believe we won the TITAN contract because we entered the competition with the belief that we only had a 5 per cent chance of winning it. I'm certain, of course, that our experience with VIKING and Matador had a lot to do with it—but rocket people are by nature superstitious."

George Bunker, however, was not superstitious, otherwise he would never have made the decision to compete for the contract. Obviously his engineering advisors were not superstitious either. Few men would be willing to stake their reputations against a 5 per cent chance of success, no matter how superstitious they might be.

Returning to Bill Purdy, who as Chief Engineer on the project was the eye in the TITAN hurricane during those early days, "That was in May of 1955 when we decided to go ahead. Our proposal was in the customer's hands by August '55. We had the letter-contract in October of '55. The start on TITAN was so rapid that before we knew it, 250 of us were out in Denver—still not quite certain what had happened.

"The job of building a manufacturing and test facility at Denver was actually larger than the job of building the rocket itself. I think that this is something few folks appreciate—the amount of effort that goes into building a facility of any sort. I can remember some of the problems we had at that time—and many of them were decidedly nonrocket problems.

"There was the matter of finding and buying the land. Mr. Bunker and Mr. Bergen came out here for the purpose. We all recognized that it was pretty important for us not to identify ourselves too obviously as Easterners. So we used some local people to help us acquire the property in the foothills of the Rocky Range, about 20 miles outside Denver. We rented offices in the Shell Building, downtown Denver, while construction work went on out in the foothills. By the time we moved out there,

about a year later, we discovered we were in a few other busi-
nesses besides rockets.

"We had to supervise a red-clay mine on the other side of the
Hogback. We also found that a good part of our attention was
being sapped by a man who held a grazing lease on our property.
So we had to patiently match our schedules with the whims of
cattle grazing around the test stands for a few years longer than
was reasonable—until the grazing lease ran out. An oil company
had a lease to drill for oil on the north boundary of our property—and they were there drilling, in spite of the tight security
surrounding our program. We also found out that there were a
few rights that even superseded those of the defense industry.
We do not hold title to a couple of pieces of land on our property. One of them is a cemetery on a little knoll that belongs to
the history of Colorado. We ran into our share of boundary disputes on the west side of the property. While we were grading
the hill for our first test stand, we ran into a quartz vein. There
was a great deal of speculation about whether we had struck
gold or not. The undercurrent of feeling was that we might be
going into the gold-mining business. We did have samples of the
quartz assayed, but to this day only two or three people know
the result—whether it was gold-bearing quartz or not. We were
ordered to continue work on the stand—and if there is gold in
that quartz it's now buried under Test Stand D-1. After the
stand was finished, we discovered that there was a fault line—a
rock stratum underground that had split because of stress
changes inside the Earth's crust—and the line ran directly from
under the stand to under our manufacturing plant. These faults
continually slip from internal pressures. We were almost afraid
to test-fire our first engine for quite a time, since we weren't certain whether we would shake the plant down to its foundations,
or cause the fault line to adjust itself from the extra energy
poured into it by the rocket engines. Apparently it adjusted itself, since we've fired enough engines by now to assume that
the probability of disaster is very low. It's pretty hard to move a

fault line, so we had to put up with it," said Purdy wryly.

Other gnat-like problems continued to divert the Martin rocket men before they could get into full production on TITAN. "One day we failed two stands wet," Purdy told me. "In more generally intelligible English that means that the fire extinguisher systems came on at two test stands as the result of a main electrical power failure. We ended up thoroughly soaking two missiles—not to mention the fact that we didn't know the cause of the power failure. It was an ordinary day, no storms or winds, yet we lost power on the entire hill, where most of the stands are located. After a long search, we finally found the cause. A bullsnake had crawled into our power substation half-way up the hill and had slithered across one of the electrical terminals. His tail was grounded and, of course, he was thoroughly fried."

THE MOLTEN SALT PROBLEM

One of the most imposing projects in establishing a totally integrated TITAN production and test complex was the heat-treating facility. This was required to fabricate the huge metal skins that form the missile's fuel and oxidizer tanks. One of the steps involved is a salt bath of sodium nitrate, which can be liquefied at temperatures between 900° and 950° Fahrenheit. Salt retains heat more efficiently and longer than most substances. Fifty thousand pounds of sodium nitrate salt were needed to treat the metal tank skins. Containing that amount of molten salt is a problem.

But let Bill Purdy describe the problem: "We had much trouble with the salt-bath containing-tank. We finally got it installed one weekend and loaded it with molten salt to check it out. Lo and behold, it sprang a leak—and the leak *had* to be at the bottom. There we were with 50,000 pounds of hot liquid salt that we didn't know what to do with. If we let it cool in the factory, it would solidify and we'd waste a lot of valuable time using air hammers to chip it away. So Scotty McCullough and a couple of boys in the shop quickly gathered up a load of 2-inch pipe. They ran a pipeline about 300 feet from the salt tank out toward the rear of the property. They scooted up the hill and borrowed a bulldozer, drove back to the factory and bulldozed an excavation where the pipeline ended. Then they pumped the salt through the pipe out into that hole in the ground. Scotty had about five men running madly up and down the pipeline with flaming blowtorches to keep the salt molten. If you know anyone who can use 25 tons of solidified salt, they're still out behind the factory."

There were also personal and emotional problems involved with the successful establishment of the Free World's first self-contained ballistic missile production complex. Many families of the Martin engineering personnel had strong misgivings about breaking up their homes in the East for a move to Denver. This included even some of the engineers, who knew that Denver had been chosen—after a survey of numerous possible locations—because it was ideally suited to the purpose. The complex site was hidden among the mountains, making it a difficult target for an enemy. It was isolated, making sabotage difficult, if not impossible. Furthermore, the thunderous blasts of rocket engines would do no damage; only the mountain goats would be disturbed. So the situation was irrevocable, but there were complaints—especially among wives. Bill Purdy was luckier than many. His wife was quite shaken by the very thought of moving to Denver—but she said nothing about her trepidation until after she got there to discover that "The Mile-High City" is actually modern and refreshing.

"She visualized Denver as a little one-street town in the middle of the plains with dust blowing down the streets and the streetlights swinging in the wind," says Purdy. "It turned out that she had had some pretty bad moments, which she kept to herself, about moving from a cosmopolitan place like Baltimore to a godforsaken place like Denver. Her mother, who lives in Baltimore, still maintains exactly that same attitude."

Nor was tragedy alien to those attempting to establish the Martin-Denver facilities. Dedication to the job and even self-sacrifice became the mood. This included almost everyone from highly trained engineers down to relatively minor technicians. A heightened example of this mood was recounted to me by Robert Blakey, who was among the original group that made the pilgrimage from Baltimore and is now Director of TITAN II Site Activation at Denver.

"I can think of one sad occasion," he said, "that was stupidly heroic. During the early days we had to run pressure tests on the propellant storage tanks in our static firing area. We would fill them with liquids to check their ability to withstand internal pressure. Then we would dry them out by spraying dry gaseous nitrogen into them under pressure. Gaseous nitrogen, of course, is quite heavy and has a smothering effect on people. One boy went down into the tank to work, before the nitrogen had been completely evacuated. Before he passed out, he managed to call for help. His buddy was on top of the tank, looking inside. He knew what would happen to him, but he went down in the tank to save his friend—and he, too, passed out. None of us physically had the time to get the proper breathing gear so that we could go down in the tank, put slings around them and haul them out the way they had gone in. It took some real fast thinking and action on the part of those of us outside the tank. We grabbed axes and chopped a big hole in the bottom of the tank and dragged them out through it. One boy was saved. The other boy that went in there first was not."

THE REASON FOR A TEST PROGRAM

Despite the problems, big, little, emotional, technological and tragic, the Martin-Denver TITAN complex was completed in record time. One year after the ground was broken, the first production missile was fired in a captive test. Three years later, the first mighty TITAN was successfully launched in flight from Cape Canaveral. The success of a maiden flight at that time was unprecedented on the Cape. It was directly due to the engineering concept behind the integrated facilities outside Denver. For there, not only are the giant ICBMs produced semi-automatically on multiple assembly lines, but they are also given the rough treatment they must ultimately encounter in flight. A huge Vertical Test Facility gives the bird its initial shakedown after it leaves the assembly line where its stages have been checked out individually. In the VTF, the two stages are mated and subjected to a series of tests that include both the mechanical (such as vibration) and the electronic. When TITAN leaves the VTF, it is a staged missile with all components integrated between the stages. It is ready for captive firing. The test stands are specially designed—allowing the stages to be erected vertically side-by-side—for sequence-firing to simulate actual flight conditions for the engines and controls. When the first stage burns out after a precisely plotted interval, the second stage ignites and burns until the planned moment of cutoff, just as it would in space. Each TITAN that leaves the Denver complex for Cape Canaveral is almost certain to fly. The tiny factor of uncertainty derives from those thousands of unforeseen possibilities that plague every missile test program. But this is the reason for a test program—to find and correct the unforeseen event. The TITAN program has suffered much less from the unforeseen than has any other big missile program.

An indication of the explosive development of Martin-Denver may be found in its employee-population. Within a year after the land was purchased, the basic group of 250 mixed executives, engineers and technicians had expanded tenfold. Today the population is 15,000.

The large cluster of modern office buildings, fabricating and power plants as well as test facilities is so well hidden that it is totally invisible from any part of the approaching highway, until a turn is made several hundred yards from the Administration Building. Then the great industrial complex bursts into view, cradled among the boulders and crags.

Within that complex nowadays may be heard the hypersonic roar of the advanced TITAN II, a much more formidable weapon-system than even the mighty TITAN I. Already operational, it is being modified as the core of TITAN III. Its roar apparently appeals to the curiosity of mountain lions, one of which moved in so close to the Administration Building that he startled hundreds of employees leaving work for their cars. He was standing on top of a big boulder above the parking lot. In a sense, it was symbolical of mankind's victory over nature. As the women screamed, the lion snarled—and retreated.

A search for such symbolism, during the early days of the Western Development Division, caused the Air Force to call up missile contractors for name suggestions derived from the gods of ancient mythology. Proposed first was Atlas, the god of Ancient Greece who kept the Universe from caving in by supporting the heavens with his hands and shoulders. Atlas was the son of Clymene and Titan—who to the Ancient Latin poets was the sun god, source of all power and life. Yet the TITAN ICBM almost came to be named Thor, the Ancient Norse god of thunder, strength and defense in war. Before the first shovelful of dirt was scooped out of the hills beyond Denver, The Martin Company was requested to conceive of a symbolical name for Project WS-107A-2. A meeting was scheduled at Headquarters of the Air Research and Development Command, then located in Baltimore. The Commander of ARDC in those days was Lt. General Thomas S. Power, presently the four-star Commander-in-Chief of SAC. He also requested that two other contractors attend the meeting with suggested names for their missiles. These were Convair-Astronautics and the Douglas Aircraft Company, which had been awarded the contract for an Intermediate Range Ballistic Missile.

Joe Rowland, Director of Public Relations at The Martin Company, was assigned the task of developing names. He presented his list of suggestions to George Bunker and Bill Bergen, both of whom were taken with "Titan." But they also liked "Thor" and proposed this as an alternate choice. Rowland, who has since retired from the company, spent considerable time at the Pratt Library poring through books for a name. He finally came up with Titan and Thor at home one evening while glancing through his children's book on mythology. The ultimate choice, of course, would have to be approved officially by the Air Force.

Seven persons attended the meeting at ARDC Headquarters. All had to be cleared for Top Secret, since the very existence of an official program to develop strategic missiles was spun thickly in the silence of security. Representing the Air Force, with authority to sanction or reject the submitted names, were Colonel A. A. Arnhym, Special Assistant to General Power, and Harold M. Helfman, an astute technical information specialist of ARDC. (Helfman is presently the Deputy Director of Information at Headquarters, Air Force Systems Command.) Speaking for Convair-Astronautics was their Director of Public Relations. Joe Rowland represented The Martin Company. The Douglas Air Craft Company sent a majority of three—Donald Douglas, Jr. himself and two public relations men, including the Vice President.

THE HUGE MISSILES ARE NAMED

The Convair man spoke first. His SM-65 missile had been the first to be contracted under Project ATLAS. He recounted the history of the missile from days of the MX-774 experiments and requested that SM-65 be officially named for the project. There was no objection from anyone. It seemed appropriate that SM-65 should carry the name ATLAS.

Rowland's turn came next for SM-68. By this time he was somewhat of an expert in Ancient Greek mythology. He knew that Titan, as father of Atlas, came first in the genealogy of the gods and was afraid that because of this, Thor might be considered more appropriate. So he withheld Thor while he argued for Titan's connotation of superior strength and invincibility. There were some minor arguments, and for several bad moments Rowland almost felt he had to pull Thor out of his pocket as an alternate. But Titan was finally accepted as the appropriate popular name for SM-68.

At this point Donald Douglas, Jr. was asked to present his choice of a symbolical name for the SM-75 IRBM. As Rowland tells the story, Douglas had been sitting through the meeting with a puzzled and uncomfortable air about him. Now he said, "Will somebody tell me what the ——— *this* is all about?" After a quick explanation, there was an awkward silence. Then Douglas said, "We are not prepared." Somewhere in his company's chain of command the original message had been garbled. He had crossed the continent from Santa Monica with two advisors, thinking all the way that the meeting had been called to discuss an entirely different missile, which already had a name.

Rowland took Douglas aside and offered him the alternate-choice name for SM-68, now officially the TITAN ICBM. Douglas felt that he should give the situation more thought, but after consulting with his Vice President of Public Relations agreed that it would be a good name to propose. And that was how the SM-75 IRBM came to be known as THOR, symbolical of thunder, strength and defense.

But no missile, regardless of the symbolical power of its name, would have meaning as a powerful deterrent to war unless it were reliably operational. To achieve such status, where, with a minimum of fuss and complexity, it becomes a viable weapon system in support of United States policy, a missile must be perfected in actual flight conditions. Given the most far-sighted managerial and engineering skills and care at its point of manufacture, no missile will ever leave the plant on operational status until it has been flight-tested to the degree that no further adjustments are required in its design. When each of many thousands of components are standardized and work together unfailingly, only then can a big missile be considered operational.

There are two kinds of flight-testing for strategic missiles: the research and development phase and the operational environment phase. Both phases demand the design and construction of new facilities peculiar to their purpose. Before the first TITAN was built, even as the Martin-Denver complex was being constructed, construction was in progress on flight-test facilities at Cape Canaveral in Florida and at Vandenberg Air Force Base in California. The former would develop TITAN, the long-range missile. When that had been accomplished, the latter would develop TITAN, the weapon system.

On the edge of Denver was Lowry Air Force Base, from where giant C-133 propjet cargo planes could airlift both stages of TITAN in a single load directly to the Cape or Vandenberg with a minimum effort. Denver was also within commuting distance for personnel of the Air Force at the Inglewood Complex alongside Los Angeles International Airport.

The almost unbelievable amount of human energy and patience that is invested in the environmental testing of an ICBM weapon system is often even transcended during the research and development flight-testing of the rocket itself at Cape Canaveral. The word "countdown" these days is a part of the common American vocabulary, yet it is doubtful that many Americans are fully aware of its connotations. A simple description of the steps involved in a flight-test countdown for TITAN I should vividly demonstrate the magnitude of effort that was expended before the first TITAN could honestly be called a bird that would fly under any conditions.

On Cape Canaveral, the Government owns the facilities, but the contractor designs them, supervises their construction and operates them. Martin Marietta is the oldest continuous resident of the Air Force Missile Test Center, overall manager of the total establishment that comprises the Atlantic Missile Range, of which Canaveral is the launching area. In that area, which could be called a huge sandbar lying between the Atlantic Ocean and the Banana River, the Martin Marietta Corporation today operates three hangars and seven missile complexes. The latter include four for TITAN, two for the MACE cruise missile and one for the Army PERSHING tactical missile. The Atlantic Missile Range itself stretches southeastwardly more than 5,000 miles through eleven islands, each equipped with ultramodern electronic and/or optical tracking devices. The names of the islands recall the "romantic" days of piracy: Grand Bahama, Eleuthera, San Salvador, Mayaguana, Grand Turk, Hispaniola, Mayaguez, Antigua, Santa Lucia, Fernando de Noronha and Ascension. The last two are below the Equator, in the South Atlantic Ocean. But they are not the end of the range, which can easily be extended an additional 5,000 miles into the Indian Ocean by the use of readily available tracking ships and aircraft. All of these tracking stations must be correlated with the Central Control Building on Cape Canaveral before a missile is launched. This is a subsidiary, but vital, aspect of any launch countdown.

The TITAN countdown begins shortly after that mighty two-stage brute touches down on the "skid strip" at the Cape, securely strapped in the huge interior of a C-133 cargo airplane from Denver. Schedule of the countdown usually covers from 10 to 12 working days. For purposes of description, we can assume the smaller number.

Until 4 hours prior to flight time, the countdown is prefixed with an "F," for "flight-control." After that, a "T" prefix is used to indicate "Time-zero."

FIRST STAGE OF THE COUNTDOWN

At F-minus-10-days, just after daylight, the Titan is unloaded from the C-133 and transported by trailer-truck to a Martin Marietta hangar. There it is given a "receiving-inspection," a visual checkout to see that all the wires are properly connected and that no components have been damaged or loosened during the long flight from Lowry Air Force Base. Next, the primer cord is installed. This is a strand of explosive cord, like a length of dynamite fuse, that is affixed to the sides of the missile's propellant tanks. It can be ignited by a radio signal from the Range Safety Officer, if he decides that the bird is off course and must be destroyed in flight. The cord then splits the tanks and the violent liquids that propel the rocket explode in a spectacular holocaust. The TITAN's first stage, after visual inspection and installation of the cord, is then transported to the

CME at the launch complex, where it is erected on the pad while inspection and cord installation are being accomplished with the second stage still in the hangar. Before the two stages can be mated on the pad, however, certain technical procedures must be performed on the second-stage engine. By the time this is done, two full working shifts have been consumed.

F-minus-9-days begins, again, just after dawn. The two stages are mated in the morning. Umbilical lines are connected to both stages from external sources to supply power and air-conditioning and to tie in the total missile with complicated electronic checkout systems. By noon this is completed. The "vertical checkout" of subsystems comes next. These include the rocket engines, hydraulic systems, fuel lines, the safety system and flight controls. First, a visual check is made. Then the fuel lines are pressurized with an inert gas and allowed to stand for a while. If the pressure drops too fast, a leak in some line is indicated. It has to be found and fixed; the whole pressurizing procedure then is performed again. This may require an extra day, thereby upsetting the countdown schedule. The electronic systems follow the hydraulic in checkout sequence. These include the precise calibration of instruments in the missile with instruments on the countdown panels in the blockhouse. The airborne radio telemetry system alone is hypercritical, since all information or technical data of the flight received by the tracking stations comes from that system. It is the heartbeat of a flight-test missile. Under the best conditions, the electronic vertical checkout devours 4 days. In the worst conditions, it can take a week or longer. When every "bug" has been flushed out of the hydraulic and electronic subsystems by technicians working steadily from dawn to night, the big TITAN bird is ready for the "Combined Systems Test." For convenience, we can say that it is now F-minus-2-days.

The Combined Systems Test is actually an electronic dry run. No fuel or oxidizer is loaded in the bird. No pressurization is applied to any subsystem except the flight-control systems. The electronic computer in the blockhouse runs through the last 5 minutes before Time-zero and simulates the lift-off and flight. The twin-barreled first-stage engine is "ignited" and held captive until it develops the right amount of "power"—then the missile is "released." The autopilot swivels the engine for control and stability until first-stage "burnout," at which point the second stage is "ignited" and "separated" to continue onward with its own engine under autopilot control. If everything performs successfully and there are no malfunctions that have to be laboriously isolated and fixed, the mighty TITAN is almost ready for an actual test flight.

At F-minus-1-day, a verification test is run on the previous day's test. This is a condensed set of procedures that check out the same subsystems in abbreviated form. At about 5 o'clock in the afternoon, again if all has gone well, the RP-1 kerosene is pumped into the fuel tanks of TITAN I.

On F-day, at T-minus-4-hours, the live countdown begins. First, all flight controls are electronically rechecked. If an unexpected bug develops, the countdown must be "held," or stopped until the trouble is discovered and corrected. The trouble could be a mysterious "glitch." More often than not, the glitch is an ironic bugaboo that sometimes takes weeks to find and is entirely inconsequential when it is found. It was born with the innovation of solid-state electronic circuitry, when transistors were introduced to replace the clumsier and less efficient vacuum tubes. It is a new word in the English language, peculiarly inspired (like so many other unfamiliar words) by the art of missilery.

An actual glitch is a momentary one-time plus or minus change in a normal wave form that is flowing across an oscilloscope screen or being traced automatically by a pen across the ruled paper in an oscillograph. It can also show as a sudden dip or peak of the needle on a meter face. In less technical terminology, a glitch is an electronic deviation of the test-recording instruments. Because it occurs only once, without warning, there are no comparative ways to determine its cause. It would be analogous to a sudden loss or surge of power that never repeats itself in your family automobile. Your fuel line is not clogged. Nothing is wrong with your carburetor. Your engine is perfectly tuned. A mechanic, after a careful inspection, suggests that you forget the whole thing.

THOSE MYSTIFYING GLITCHES

But missilemen cannot afford to ignore a glitch. Apart from the several millions of dollars involved in a big ICBM test vehicle, the nation's security is at stake. The glitch may result from a flutter of voltage in the power lines feeding the recording instruments themselves. Even a brief, abrupt change in the electrical potential of the ground could cause it. Quite often these are the causes. It may not be in the missile at all. Yet there is always the haunting possibility that a glitch presages some unforeseen serious trouble, that it is a hint of imperfection in an otherwise well-engineered and tested prototype weapon. Like a flutter of pulse during physical exertion, it may be a symptom that something is wrong with the heart of the system. Its cause MUST be found before the countdown can continue. Finding it with precision is often similar to searching the sea for a drop of fresh water.

Still, the glitches are found ultimately, and the big birds soar down the missile ranges because of the tireless effort, ingenuity and skill of the test personnel.

At T-minus-40-minutes, the liquid oxygen (dubbed "lox") is loaded into the oxidizer tanks of TITAN I. Continuously it has to be "topped," or replenished to maintain a certain level in the tanks, since it is supercold and boils away through vent valves as a gas at normal temperatures.

The Complete Missile Erector is lowered at T-minus-20-minutes. All personnel are evacuated from the launch area because of the explosion hazard, as the high-pressure containers in the missile are automatically raised to full pressure. This pressure will control the fuel flow, the lox flow and activate various devices in TITAN I.

At T-minus-2½-minutes, the liquid oxygen-topping procedure is discontinued. People inside the blockhouse, protected by steel blast-doors and a tremendous thickness of reinforced concrete, are carefully watching the lonely giant of a missile through periscopes and by closed-circuit television. The eyes of technical specialists are sharply focused on their respective instruments, recording devices and console indicators. The clocks are smoothly counting down the time to zero. Everything looks perfect, but anything *could* still go wrong.

Typical of the human concentration in the blockhouse as a countdown proceeds toward the ignition point was a response of Major Fountain Hutchinson, Air Force Chief of the TITAN Test Operations Office on Cape Canaveral. The little story was recalled for me by his boss, Colonel Edmund Novotny, military head of all TITAN testing at the Air Force Missile Test Center. Before quoting him, it is necessary to know that there are four periscopes in each TITAN blockhouse: one is manned by an officer from Colonel Novotny's branch, another by the Pad Safety Officer and two by Martin Marietta personnel. They all wear headsets like a telephone switchboard operator and report moment by moment the test rocket's condition to a teletype operator who transmits these reports continuously to their various headquarters, such as the Ballistic Systems Division in California, Martin-Denver and the Range Safety Officer on the Cape. The reports are also monitored by everyone inside the blockhouse.

"Our office always has a man at the periscope," Novotny began. "He acts as our eyes, because the television receivers are not nearly as sharp in detail, although we can watch them while listening to him. Whoever it may be—we rotate these men—he usually falls into a kind of monotone chant. He's watching the missile more than thinking of himself. On this particular occasion, Major Hutchinson was at the periscope and was reporting: 'Lift-off . . . Looks good . . . Going good . . . It's going good . . . Looks real good . . . Real good . . .' And just about the time we were getting elated and cheering each other a bit, about 50 seconds after lift-off, he said: 'Going good . . .

Good . . . She blew up . . .' He said this without changing his expression one bit. The girl on the teletype machine was also so concentrated that she sent his intonation as one word—'itblewup'—out to the West Coast."

Of course nobody on a test program likes to see a missile explode, whether the explosion results spontaneously from an unforeseen malfunction or whether the Range Safety Officer decides to destroy the bird for the safety of all who might be endangered. But it's something that missilemen learn to live with. Quoting George Smith, who at one time was General Manager of the Martin Canaveral Division: "The most difficult task that I ever faced, I think, was the first time I had to phone Bill Bergen in Baltimore and tell him we had just lost a missile. It only got so far off the stand, fell back down, burned up the stand and blew up. I had the feeling then that an old cliché applied—'For want of a nail, the horse was lost.' But the second time we lost a missile, it wasn't as hard. When I phoned the company president, he actually was a little bit more understanding than he was that first time on the phone. We were learning the hard way to expect the unexpected."

A very human example of how the unexpected problem is sometimes discovered and solved was a story told to me by Don Herron, presently Director of Public Relations in the Washington, D.C. Office of Martin Marietta Corporation. At the time, he held the same position with Martin-Denver. He, along with the Denver Division's Chief Engineer, Dr. Albert C. Hall, had gone down to Cape Canaveral to watch a TITAN experimental launching. Herron was exceedingly nervous on the morning of the launch. But I'll let him tell his own story.

"I guess I was about as good a guy as anybody," he started, "at chewing handkerchiefs or nails or twisting things—pieces of paper or anything else. And on this particular morning of a launch, Al Hall and I sat down to breakfast in the Polaris Motel. It was only a couple of hours before Time-Zero, and I was all keyed up.

"I ordered a breakfast which included pancakes, sausage and

coffee. As we chatted away, the waitress brought the coffee and the syrup for my pancakes. So, talking with Al, I quickly picked up the syrup—and poured it in the coffee. Everybody guffawed and I laughed—you know, a joke on a very stupid guy who was being nervous. The waitress was alert and was already enroute with a new cup of coffee before I could ask her. She was chuckling. At this point, Al had started to read his newspaper. So again I picked up the syrup and very carefully poured it—into the second cup of coffee. By then I felt that I deserved to drink the gooey coffee—which I did."

Don Herron's nervousness was unfortunately prophetic. That morning, the test-missile exploded on the pad. It was a mysterious explosion that seemed to indicate something was seriously wrong with the rocket engine of the first stage of the missile. If this were true, it would require considerable redesigning of the engine and thus delay the program. At the time of the explosion, Herron was standing atop the Press Platform at Cape Canaveral, which is out in an open field about three miles from the TITAN flight-test pads. Dr. Al Hall was approximately three miles again away from Herron, in another direction. He was at the Range Safety Officer's position. Both he and Herron saw a small, quick flash just prior to the explosion. This suggested to them that the destruct-system in the missile had been triggered, but the "Quick-look Data" indicated an engine malfunction. Besides, the Range Safety Officer had not closed the destruct-switch. Let Don Herron continue in his own words:

"Apart from the Quick-look Data, which only expresses a trend or an indication, the most important means to determine the cause or causes of failures are the detailed film-data and the actual motion pictures themselves of the launch.

"The data on film would not be processed and ready until the middle of the night or early the next day. The movie footage— from a variety of cameras focused on the missile from several different angles and distances—would not be ready for a couple of days. These would include both normal-speed footage and some very, very slow-motion footage. The latter, of course, would be of particular interest because of the split-second action that took place.

"Anyway, Sunday morning finally came around and we all assembled at the Space Technology Laboratories Offices where the projection room was located. The detailed technical data had been processed by this time and still gave no indication other than that of an engine failure. Aerojet-General, the engine manufacturer, was obviously quite concerned.

"The first reel was shown and all we could see—even at extremely slow motion—was a big ball of flame developing. It seemed to be coming from the bottom of the bird. Nothing that we viewed even faintly indicated the thing that was hitting me and Dr. Hall—which was that the flash we had noticed occurred at a very precise point, at just one particular area on the side of the bird. So we kept saying, 'Well, maybe the next reel will show it. What we're looking at now could have been photographed from the wrong angle.

"We kept saying this throughout six reels. By that time, everybody was staring at us like we were the boy who cried wolf too often. Few really even considered our analysis to be faintly logical.

"Then came the last reel. The projector was started. And abruptly—boy-oh-boy! there it was: just as clear and simple to see and understand as anything *could* be!

"There on the external conduit—that raised strip that runs the length of the TITAN—in which is located the primer cord (the explosive charge in rope-form that's used to split the tanks open and destroy the missile during malfunctions)—there we could see the smoky puff of the little charge detonator that ignites the cord. Then we could just watch the cord strip the tank open and the huge explosion taking place. All this happened in a split-second of time, but we viewed it over a minute or so because of the very slow motion of the footage. The missile had not destroyed itself. It was destroyed by the destruct-system going off accidentally. It wasn't the engine.

"After an extensive series of tests compressed into a week back at Denver, we were able to duplicate the condition in our Vertical Test Facility, using another tank. We proved what seemed to be the case. The combination of engine-thrust, of the explosive bolts blowing all at once at the moment of release for the launch, plus the 220,000 pounds of weight of the missile—all of these mighty forces coming into play at the same precise instant —produced a shock wave that moved with lightning speed across the engine compartment and focused itself on an electrical relay that was an important part of the destruct-system. It triggered that relay, which in turn destroyed the missile by activating the destruct-system. This was certainly a completely, but thoroughly unexpected accident!"

It is the discovery of the unexpected that makes a test program important. And it is the unexpected that makes the countdown a drawn out, tedious and revealing procedure.

After the countdown, comes the countup—as the test bird leaves the pad for its flight through space. The countup is made by adding time rather than subtracting it from "F" or "T." In fact, no "F" is required. The actual flight takes minutes, not days. Nevertheless, in those 30-odd minutes of flight a glitch might be recorded that would consume weeks, sometimes months to define. A vivid example of something very nearly like a glitch that occurred during countup was given to me by Brigadier General John L. McCoy, the current Program Director on TITAN at the Air Force Ballistic Systems Division.

General McCoy's anecdote pertains to an early "Lot M" TITAN I missile. "The 'M' Series of TITANS comprised seven test vehicles that were modified to carry and perfect the all-inertial guidance system intended for TITAN II. This was the new system developed for the Air Force by the Massachusetts Institute of Technology and being manufactured by the AC Sparkplug Division of General Motors, since the first all-inertial system developed for TITAN by American Bosch-Arma had been turned over to the ATLAS ICBM for jam-proof guidance—as was already described by General Schriever in the previous chapter. The new system was more advanced and was controlled by a miniaturized airborne IBM electronic computer. The "glitch" occurred in the computer during a flight down the Atlantic Missile Range.

MISSILE DETECTIVE STORY

As McCoy described the situation: "This would make a really good detective story, if it weren't so technical. All our 'detectives' had to work with was one tiny drop in electrical energy from the computer that was tape-recorded at a ground tracking station. Added to this was the fact that the missile fell short of its target. The reason was mysterious and the clues almost nonexistent. Skipping the technical details, they finally traced the defect to a soldering procedure. There were 1,600 connections between small electronic parts in the computer. Forty of them were soldered in such a way that the heat created little air bubbles in the solder, changing the electrical resistance at a critical point. It was like bubbles in the brain. The computer thought the missile had less velocity to make up than was actually so—if the missile was to accelerate enough to hit the target. So the computer turned off the vernier rockets on stage two and the TITAN fell short.

"Since then, of course, the soldering techniques have been changed. The very next 'Lot M' TITAN that we fired, the computer worked so well that the missile struck right in the middle of the Splash Net."

As an aside, the Splash Net is a small area of the South Atlantic Ocean staked out with submerged hydrophone-type instruments to record the impact of ICBM Re-entry Vehicles off Ascension Island. The goal of a guidance system test flight is to strike the Splash Net at dead center.

Another aside: the lethal accuracy of TITAN II is due in large measure to the vast experience and engineering courage of Paul Blasingame, who left his professorship at the Air Force Academy specifically to direct the development and manufacture of the new MIT all-inertial ICBM guidance system at the AC Sparkplug Division in Milwaukee. Dr. Blasingame obviously

was the best, if not the only, man for the intricate job of corre-
lating the industrial aspects with the military requirement of
foolproof accurate guidance. He had worked on both sides of
the desk and was closely acquainted with all the responsible
TITAN engineering personnel at Martin-Denver as well as at
the Ballistic Systems Division of USAF. It was a case again of
his changing jobs on the basis of how important his contribution would be to national security.

Such contributions can be exhausting as well as dramatic.
For instance, during each test flight of a TITAN from Cape Canaveral there are recorded about eighteen miles of magnetic
tape. Signals from the rocket sent by radio at every second of
countup are frozen in this tape for analysis. Some 300 measurements are made, ranging from skin temperature to fuel level in
the tanks, from first- and second-stage burnout to separation
of the Re-entry Vehicle as it falls from space onto its target inside
the Splash Net. The tape has to be translated, since it contains
only an audible jumble of coded signals that cannot be defined
by the ear. Immediately after a TITAN flight, the tape recordings are rushed to the Data Processing Laboratory of Martin
Marietta's Canaveral Division, where they are fed into playback
machines that contain electronic discriminating devices to separate the compressed signals and restore them to their original
electrical energy level. Then they are transcribed from sound to
lines on graph paper—miles of it. Certain measurements are
transcribed to rolls of sensitized film and developed. This
method was the one referred to as Quick-look Data by Don
Herron. Interpreting these wavy and spiked lines on film or
paper is similar to, but much more difficult than, interpreting
the functions of a human heart by analyzing an electrocardio-
graph. It is also considerably more wearing.

Yet the Martin Marietta laboratory is merely supplemental to
the Technical Laboratory of USAF at Patrick Air Force Base fif-
teen miles south of Cape Canaveral. Here the total data received from all down-range tracking stations is processed and
correlated. After 10 or 12 hours of intensive work, the two labora-

tories are in a position to compare results. Meanwhile, the Martin-Canaveral Lab has made many duplicate copies of the transcribed recordings so that each of the associate contractors on the TITAN program can analyze the performance of their subsystems in flight. Prominent among these are the Aerojet-General Corporation (rocket engines), the AVCO Corporation (Re-entry Vehicle) and the guidance system people with their various subcontractors. A duplicate copy is also airlifted to Martin-Denver, home of the TITAN, for analysis. Intensive consultations between the numerous technical experts concerned, both civilian and military, finally produce a sharply detailed, integrated portrait of the flight. Certain subsystems have proved themselves; others will have to be modified or changed for the next flight.

BUT ALMOST ANYTHING CAN HAPPEN

The foregoing simplified description of a countdown and test flight can be applied in equal or lesser degree to all missiles and rocket-borne space vehicles in the research and development stage. Technical problems and frustrations are accepted by missilemen as an inevitable hallmark of their profession. The only thing usually unanticipated is the cause of the problem or frustration. It can be almost anything.

Moisture might condense in a valve on a humid day. As 300°-below-zero liquid oxygen reaches that valve on its way to the rocket combustion chamber, the valve would quickly freeze in an open or shut position. Grit or gravel in the same lox line might cause the rocket to explode after lift-off. Engine vibration could shake up the grit violently enough to cause a forceful impact against the sides of a tank or pipeline, thereby detonating the liquid oxygen. Oil or grease can create the ignition of lox. In fact, at Cape Canaveral once, according to rumor, a rattlesnake crawled into a feed line from a lox storage tank, and its oily skin caused a sizable explosion when the liquid oxygen began to be pumped through the line to feed the oxidizer tank of a missile. A peach pit caused a minor explosion by detonating lox at the Liquid Rocket Engine Plant of Aerojet-General in Sacramento. When liquid oxygen boils off into gaseous oxygen (called "gox" in the trade), its volume expands 800 times within a brief period. If it is confined in an area from which it cannot escape, the explosive results should be easy to imagine.

Such problems are not inherent with TITAN II. Its oxidizer is storable at normal temperatures. It is also simpler and more powerful than TITAN I. A few random comparisons between these two giants of America's missile arsenal should make the point. TITAN I has 91 valves and regulators; TITAN II has 16. There are 322 pieces of Ground Support Equipment for the operational TITAN I weapon system; TITAN II requires only 35 units of such equipment. Launching a TITAN I demands 230 separate functions; TITAN II can be launched after 23 functions. The number of power-control operations in flight are 220 for TITAN I and only 25 for TITAN II. The quantity of relays and umbilical connections in TITAN II have each been reduced by 87 per cent over TITAN I. Yet TITAN I itself is a much simpler ICBM than the ATLAS.

TITAN II, like TITAN I, has the distinction of a completely successful maiden test flight from Cape Canaveral. But it can boast three additional distinctions as well. It traveled farther than any other missile on an initial flight—5,000 miles. It was the first fully integrated ICBM with liquid propellants to be launched in an initial flight. The usual case is a step-by-step testing of basic subsystems through a series of flights. During its maiden flight it carried one of the heaviest Re-entry Vehicles ever placed atop any missile on any flight. Its first-stage rocket engine alone generated a power equivalent to that of roughly 22,000 automobiles. Carrying the lighter weight, but nonetheless devasting, nuclear-primed RVs that are standard for AT-LAS and TITAN I, it could destroy strategic targets halfway around the world from the United States. It can deliver the new superheavy RV with accuracy on positions beyond 6,000 miles away.

"What we're doing with TITAN II," an Air Force officer told

me, "is making wars old-fashioned." That was Colonel Bill Mc-
Ginty, Director of Information at Headquarters, Air Force
Systems Command, explaining in his colorful way that the
TITAN weapon system is the most powerful deterrent to war on
Earth.

Among the numerous advantages of its great power is the
capability of TITAN II to carry Electronic Countermeasure devices, along with its destructive nuclear payload. Such ECM
devices could confuse an enemy's ability to locate the missile,
even if he had the means to destroy it before it reached its target. In simpler words, TITAN II will carry its own decoys to
divert the enemy's defenses while its RV strikes into a selected
target.

The high reliability and strength of TITAN II were the reasons for its choice by the National Aeronautics and Space Administration as the launch vehicle of Project Gemini. This is
NASA's follow-on to Project Mercury in its program to land a
crew safely on the moon and bring its members back to Earth
before 1970. The Gemini capsule will carry two men in orbit
around the Earth for extended periods to test the effects of
weightlessness on human functions. A manned lunar voyage
might take about a week, depending on the trajectory chosen,
and the moonbound crew must be able to function alertly in
order to stay alive and make a successful lunar landing. Gemini
will train men not only to operate skillfully in the spaceflight
medium but will also help to condition their bodies to the
rigors of the alien space environment. Most importantly, from
a military viewpoint, the Project Gemini experiments will provide scientific and engineering knowledge about the intricacies
of rendezvous as well as docking techniques in space. For if
manned orbital space stations are ever required to maintain the
military superiority of the Free World, then previous experience
with rendezvous and docking is an absolute necessity. The pilots
of space personnel- and cargo-carriers would have to know how
to intercept an orbital station traveling at about 18,000 miles
an hour in a near-orbit and slightly less than a thousand miles an

hour in a distant synchronous orbit. After interception, their craft would need to be carefully maneuvered to a landing dock on the station. In the case of NASA's peaceful exploration of the moon, the lunar landing vehicle, called LEM, for "Lunar Exploration Module," would later have to rendezvous with the mother ship (which would remain in orbit about the moon) and dock on it. Otherwise, the moon explorers could not return to Earth. The Gemini rendezvous and docking tests will be accomplished with an unmanned Lockheed-made Agena-B satellite placed in a circular orbit by a General Dynamics-built ATLAS and controlled from the ground by radio.

But the Martin Marietta-constructed TITAN II will make the core of the experiment possible. The entire experiment, of course, is possible only because of the dedication and vision that sparked the United States Air Force to call upon and work closely with the imaginative skills of private-enterprise industry. Out of this came the ATLAS, TITAN and Agena.

A RECORD FOR INDUSTRY

The TITAN II created something of a record for the Martin Marietta Corporation, integrating contractor, the Aerojet-General Corporation, rocket-engine associate, and the AC Sparkplug Division of GM, associate for the foolproof guidance system. From issuance of the contract to time of the first successful flight test was a mere interval of 19 months. In pre-World War II days, the interval between contract and production of a much less complicated weapon usually was at least a half-dozen years.

Yet spectacular as this record may seem, it did not come easy for these companies. Behind it, of course, was the escalating experience with TITAN I, which had originally absorbed 75,000 man-hours for the production of each test-missile. Ultimately this was reduced to 35,000 man-hours, less than half the time, per every TITAN I that came off the production lines. One of the gravest unknown quantities that faced both the engine manufacturer and integrating contractor was ignition of a big liquid-fuel rocket engine in the thin air of near-space, after the second stage separated from the main TITAN booster. The solution of that problem was a tremendous bonus to TITAN II technology. It determined the feasibility of a maiden flight for the more advanced TITAN that would test the totally integrated ICBM flight system.

Experience acquired with the VANGUARD second-stage ignition also helped considerably. Although it had a much smaller engine, it used the same fuel and a similar oxidizer to TITAN II.

But in the early days of production planning at Denver, nobody was quite certain of the engineering techniques that must be involved with second-stage ignition, using lox as an oxidizer. Several ambitious test plans were ingeniously devised, then abandoned when they proved either too unwieldy or too expensive.

Bill Purdy described one of these as follows. "In the planning stages, problems always seem generally smaller. At least, your sincere feeling is that they're smaller. The TITAN Program was based on certain precepts, one of which was that we must do as much testing as possible on the ground, prior to flight, as was physically possible. Under that precept we designed a free-fall tower. It was to simulate the separation of the two stages. According to our calculations, it should be 325 feet high. And in this tower, we were going to fire up the first stage—all 300,000 pounds of thrust in it—and let it run up the tower for about a second, then cut it off. We designed some gigantic brakes which we expected to use to slow down the booster while we ignited the second stage and let it separate. Again we had brakes to slow it down before it went right on out the top of the tower. Just to play things safely, we designed the top of the tower with a sieve-like network of structural steel. We felt that if the brakes failed, the steel network would stop the missile.

"Well, the whole thing was very easy to contemplate in a rough preliminary design—but when we got to the point of worrying about specific details, about how in the dickens we were going to bring this monster into being, all of the problems associated with it suddenly flooded us. We and the Air Force came to our senses and canceled it. We decided that we ought to be able to depend on our engineering judgment instead."

George Bunker told me about another early plan, equally ambitious. "We considered as one of our most difficult problems," he said, "the separation of the second stage and start-up of the second-stage engine in a vacuum. This had never been done before and we found that there was no practical way to simulate it. So we took another approach. We planned to build a vacuum chamber that would simulate the upper atmospheric conditions. Inside this chamber we planned to fire the rocket engines in sequence. But after careful consideration, we saw that the chamber would have to be of such a fantastic size and would cost such a tremendous amount that it would be completely impractical to build it. We decided finally to depend on our people's technical skills and engineering imagination. These could be tested in actual flight."

Unfortunately, small things intervened to prevent these from being tested in actual flight for a long time. Each of the first four flights of TITAN I was a huge success. Three of these were flights of a live first stage carrying a dummy second stage filled with water to simulate the proper payload weight. The fourth flight actually accomplished stage separation, again with a dummy second stage, which was exploded away from the first stage at its top altitude in order to measure the cleanness and distance of separation. There was no ignition of a second-stage engine. In fact, that dummy stage carried no engine. But valuable information was learned from the experiment. It led most of the TITAN I engineering personnel to have high hopes that a successful separation and ignition of a live second stage could be accomplished on the next flight test.

SMALL MALFUNCTIONS
CAUSE DRAMATIC "FAILURES"

The first attempt at a live fully staged flight ended in disaster—not because anything was wrong with the stage-separation concepts of the engineers at Denver. A relay chattered closed from vibration, causing a sequence of events which ended in the missile destroying itself before it could rise high enough for second-stage separation and ignition. This was what George Smith meant when he said that he had felt "for want of a nail, the horse was lost." Small unanticipated malfunctions dogged TITAN I through 8 months of attempts to flight-test its live second stage.

As George Bunker describes the situation: "We and the Air Force had complete confidence in the technical aspects of TITAN. But still we were having troubles. Though they were minor technically, they were dramatic and fearful from the standpoint of our burning up a rocket or losing a launching pad. And it seemed that the one thing we could do, the ultimate thing in an organizational sense, would be for me to go out to Denver and take charge of the operation. The idea was that I would stay there as long as it took, not only to get the program on the road but to buy enough time and enough reduced external pressure for the people who were responsible for doing the job so that they could get it accomplished."

"By 'external pressure,'" I asked, "do you mean the public attitude?"

"Yes. The public attitude, the attitude that the Air Force had to deal with in the Appropriations Committee, the pressures that came down from the Department of Defense, from the Chief of Staff of the Air Force, and went all through the Ballistic Missile Division and ultimately ended up on the back of the contractor.

"So the reason I went to Denver was to provide the psychological force, the psychological support that everyone needed. After all, I was the Chief Executive Officer. I was in a real sense a party to everything. If we decided that next Wednesday we would fly Missile Number Ten, or if we decided to cancel a subcontract with a company that wasn't doing a successful job— and that cancellation meant a 3-week delay to the program or an additional expenditure, I was in a full sense a partner to those decisions. Nobody would be subject to criticism by me because I was at least as responsible—in many cases, more responsible—than he. And this took a great deal of pressure off the project engineers, the quality-control people and even off the subcontracting manufacturers."

Bunker's method of cracking no whips but sharing blame for failures as well as praise for successes set a calmer mood in those hectic days when the misinformed were loudly calling for the TITAN Program to be canceled in favor of ATLAS. He added nothing to the actual engineering design of TITAN. His vital contribution was an intelligently considered calmness. His philosophy was that it would be better to take an extra 3 weeks or a month in preparations for a scheduled test and be reasonably certain of success than to rush things, meet the indicated schedule—and suffer failure. Because of this philosophy, the TITAN program *did* ultimately catch up with time lost in superficial failures and stay on schedule.

Typical of Bunker's approach was an action taken by him and Purdy. "We noted," he said, "that some of the other test programs spent not days, but weeks and months in hangars preparing their missiles for firing after they were sent to the Cape. Our program, after all, was more accelerated than the one that had gone before it. Albeit, we had some advantages because we learned from their successes and failures. Nevertheless, ours was a much more accelerated program. So we decided to try a new approach to management.

"We had two basic areas of problems—engineering and development at Denver; launching and flight-testing at the Cape. And we decided that the way to handle things was to put them under separate management, each being responsible to Mr. Purdy and me. The work assignment for Denver was to deliver to Cape Canaveral a rocket in fireable condition. It was the responsibility of the Canaveral group to accept that missile as being in fireable condition, to put it on the test stand and to fly it. We ran into quite a little opposition from all sides. This was not traditional. There were now two lines of communication, instead of one. But it finally proved to be the right way to get things done efficiently and fast."

The first TITAN sent down to Cape Canaveral under the new approach appeared to be in perfect condition at Denver. It was given a visual inspection in a hangar at Canaveral and appeared again to be in satisfactory condition. But when the second-stage engine was being prepared for mating of the two stages on the launch pad, technical problems were discovered. The Canaveral crew, to save time, decided to request Aerojet-General to airlift a replacement engine from California. This was vetoed by Bunker after consultation with Purdy. The new engine would not have been statically tested in a captive sequence firing at Denver (an important aspect of the unified development program).

TWO ROUND TRIPS FOR TITAN

"They were going to have a certain number of engineers and technicians fly down from Denver and change the engine," said Bunker. "But Purdy and I made them take the missile off the launch pad, put it back in the C-133, fly it to Denver, place it on the test stand in Denver and change the engine there, along with a sequence of other things that had to be done in making the change. At Denver they made the change, checked it out and sent it back to the Cape. When it arrived at the Cape, it still wasn't satisfactory. So we ordered them to send it back to Denver again. It made two round trips before it was ultimately fired. Then it was a success. At the Cape, they've always said since that this missile traveled farther by airplane than it did on its actual flight."

Bunker interrupted my laughter. "But this was extremely important. We thought so then. We think so now. It's the approach that has given us such a good test-flight record on TITAN. And more currently, on the PERSHING missile for the Army."

It was the approach that finally broke the hard-luck run of minor malfunctions and gave the TITAN engineers a chance to test the validity of their strength and imaginations. Again, a countdown was in progress on a live two-stage TITAN I. The air of expectancy and tension can best be expressed through those who were waiting for Time-zero at Denver, almost 2,000 air miles from Cape Canaveral.

The personalities of those involved were vividly etched by their emotional reactions to the countdown. The two key men at Denver—George Bunker, the Corporation's Chief Executive Officer, and Dr. Albert C. Hall, Director of Engineering—reacted as differently as storm and sunshine. As always before, even if TITAN lifted off the pad perfectly, there was no physical precedent to indicate that the second stage would separate and ignite as programmed. But let George Bunker tell about this particular countdown.

"I remember sitting in my office listening at the telephone and it got down to T minus a few seconds and then there was a 'hold.' It was rescheduled to something like T-minus-2-minutes. After that it got down to minus 30 seconds. Another hold. They went back to about T-minus-4-minutes. I just couldn't stand being alone any longer.

"So I went out and walked around. I didn't see anybody on my floor. I went upstairs and there were maybe thirty-five to forty engineers standing around the classified teletype machine. The messages were all coded, but when the count got down close to lift-off, the messages would be decoded as fast as they came through the teletype. Of course, in many, many cases we would all be down at Canaveral in the blockhouse. But on this special day, for one reason or another, many of us had to remain in Denver. It was too much.

"So I started looking for Dr. Hall—and couldn't find him. I finally noticed that his office door was closed, so I opened it and went in. He was sitting there, bent over his desk with his head on his arm, listening to the telephone, the direct line to the blockhouse at Canaveral. He heard the door open and close and looked up. 'Al,' I said, 'I just couldn't stand being alone any longer.' He said, 'I just couldn't stand being with people!' But he added, 'Sit down. You're welcome.'

"He sat there silently for awhile, listening, and then he began to interpret for me: T minus so many seconds, and so forth un-till lift-off. We sat there and counted the firing duration of the first stage. Then we got to the critical point of engine cutoff. We waited. It took a little time. Actually it was seconds, but it seemed like hours. Finally, Al said, 'The second stage ignited.' It was a quiet statement. He removed the telephone from where it had rested on his arm and placed it on his lap. He never listened to another word."

That moment was the culmination of many severe responsi-bilities for the two men. They and their engineering staff, as Bunker puts it, were "the principal architects" on TITAN. The visible drama of their accomplishment overwhelmed a multi-tude of invisible managerial details, without which nothing would have been accomplished. Awareness and correlation of these details are what provide free-enterprise industry with its vitality. Control of the details has nothing to do with political or philosophical prejudices, as it does in the USSR. It depends entirely upon the freedom of individuals to act upon the basis of their professional experience and creative imaginations. In-tuition, deplored by the Communists as "mysticism," also plays its very important role in the free-enterprise management of industry. For awareness is often inspired by intuition bul-warked with experience.

BUNKER DEFINES GOOD MANAGEMENT

An example of management problems at the Martin Marietta Corporation (which typify those of the entire United States aerospace industry) was simply stated to me by George Bunker. "The basic problem," he said, "is to administer. I mean, to see that the engineering organization functions properly; to see that the procurement requirements which develop as a result of your engineering are properly processed through the procurement group; to make certain that you have the proper bidding proce-dures for subcontractors and that you select good ones; that you monitor them carefully; that you have a quality-control sys-tem of high competence in your own house—as well as out in the field; and to make sure that when engineering changes are required—and they come by the hundreds in the aerospace industry—that each one is followed through all the way down the line. It is one thing for an engineer to change his requirements and quite another thing to make certain the change goes out through every channel. The procurement people must understand it so that they can have the subcontractor understand it, and he must make the change precisely. Otherwise you could end up with hundreds of thousands of dollars worth of subcontracted components that are just fine when they're inspected. They exactly meet all specifications—except we changed those specifications 6 weeks ago!"

The foregoing statement gains considerable significance when one is aware that the TITAN Weapon System brought together actually several hundred subcontractors and suppliers, the majority of which had never before worked together.

It gains even more significance when one learns that during 1961 the taxpayer was saved $16.5 million dollars on officially budgeted costs for the TITAN Program. The Martin Marietta goal for 1962 was a cost reduction of 40 million dollars on TITAN. It was met. The Martin-Orlando section of Martin Company Division has reduced the cost of the BULLPUP air-to-ground missile by more than 70 per cent since production began there in 1958.

Cost reduction is vigorously pursued by both the Air Force and the total aerospace industry. It is continuously promoted and monitored by the Department of Defense. But it is not an easy accomplishment. Its most important requirement is astute and ingenious management, military as well as civilian. Its need was aptly expressed by Brigadier General M. C. Smith, Air Force Director of System Services. He was speaking to another Smith—George E., presently General Manager of Martin-Denver—at a luncheon to make subcontractors cost-reduction conscious. "This task is deadly serious," said General Smith, "and vitally essential to our national security, the security of the Free World and to our national economic welfare. The key criteria to our success is meeting technical and operational objectives with reliable systems produced on schedule at minimum cost."

The Martin Company Division of Martin Marietta has continuously achieved General Smith's objectives ever since George Bunker was placed in command of the corporation. Ninety-four per cent of all defense projects have been completed on time or ahead of schedule. Ninety-seven per cent were produced at cost objectives or below. TITAN II, for instance, is produced at one-third less than the cost of TITAN I, yet it is almost twice as powerful and ten times as reliable as the earlier TITAN. Its first flight-test models were manufactured with an investment of half the man-hours needed to produce the early TITAN Is.

In a freely competitive society, quality production at lower cost is a *must* for a company's survival. The TITAN SM-68 weapon system and its integrating contractor are virile examples of the vitality inherent in the entire free-enterprise industry. The Martin Company Division of Martin Marietta has figuratively traversed interstellar distances since the days of the VIKING Research Rocket, when the company seesawed at the edge of bankruptcy. Since that time, they have delved into and conquered many advanced fields of science and technology. Their original hard-core group of scientists and engineers, learning new approaches to management, has stimulated the company's successful expansion into a diversity of fields. The first nuclear power plants in the world to supply power for satellites in orbit were designed and built by them. The Space Administration called on them to produce the world's first Lunar Handbook, a technical treatise that covers all engineering aspects of moon exploration—from Earth launch to lunar landing and return, from tracking and communications to solar physics and special missions. They have also designed and manufactured a lunar spaceship simulator on NASA contract to train space pilots for the long voyage to the moon—a voyage that in 20 years will seem short indeed by comparison with the longer manned ones to the planets. In this respect, they have been awarded a contract to study the feasibility of the NOVA rocket, the monster that may someday boost men on their way to Mars from the Earth.

Roswell Gilpatrick, Deputy Secretary of Defense, once wrote the following: "The Department of Defense and the aerospace industry share the mutual responsibility of keeping our Nation technologically ahead of any possible enemy." This has been consistently and progressively accomplished during the past decade. But technological superiority is like a river: beyond the rapids, on the calm side of an unexpected bend may lie fantastic discoveries to aid an enemy—instead of us. Everything depends on who gets there first. The threats that must be anticipated and neutralized during the next decade constitute the theme of the following chapter.

7.

If DEMOCRACY is to LIVE

"One of us must go to the grave. We do not want to go to the grave. They do not want to go to their grave either. So what can be done? We must push them to their grave."

—*Nikita Sergeyevich Khrushchev*

IN THE above remark, the "they," of course, refers to the Free World, with special emphasis upon the strongest member of that democratic community—the United States of America. Another remark by Premier Khrushchev was more widely publicized: "Whether you like it or not, history is on our side. We will bury you!" These boastful threats of the Communist leader are both a figure of speech and real. He actually believes, as Lenin once said, that "capitalism is its own gravedigger." But realistically he does not intend to wait for that day of doom. By every method available to him, he intends, in his own word, to "push" it. His past and present actions show that he means to engage us on a range of battlefields that extend from guerrilla tactics in the jungles to outer space, from the psychological intimidation of our allies to a race for military superiority.

His scientists have tested nuclear devices estimated to be in a yield spectrum of between 50 and 60 megatons. Whether or not he and his comrades will someday be able to deliver these super-heavy devices to a distant target is beside the point. The very

219

presence of such technology in our self-designated enemy's hands *is* a future threat to the Free World. The Communists are indeed out to bury us when and as soon as they are able. Up till now they have been forced to follow the path of subtlety—economic infiltration and propaganda to build a benign-power image among the uncommitted nations, the insidious stimulation of "wars of national liberation," spectacular feats of space technology, some real, some exaggerated, that outperform the steady efforts of the United States. Yet the one thing all Communists understand is a show of genuine force. If at any one place their own force is not superior, they retreat to nibble away at another democratic stronghold. It is a guerrilla approach to the Space Age. But guerrillas never tire, and ultimately they become strong enough or their enemy is weakened enough for them to conquer. A sudden technological breakthrough on their part—and they ceaselessly work for this, absorbing and adapting all the technical data they can get from the Free World through espionage or the open literature—could have horrifying results.

If the Soviets should ever achieve the capability of launching into orbit big thermonuclear devices (100 to 300 megatons or more), they would not have to worry about accurate guidance systems for missiles to carry smaller H-bombs directly to a target. They would not even have to worry about retaliation from the Strategic Air Command. For the conflagration they could cause might conceivably catch everyone by surprise. Today we can detect and identify, either as known or unknown, every satellite placed in orbit. But we cannot determine whether a satellite is peacefully scientific or hostile as a weapon of offense. One day the Kremlin could publicly announce the launching of several satellite experiments for peaceful research. They do this continually without stimulating a SAC alert. And if on this particular day the Soviet satellites were carrying huge thermonuclear devices around the world, we would have no precise way of knowing this, unless it had been anticipated some years earlier and we had developed equipment to inspect those satellites. If we had not anticipated such a possibility—and Communists are not renowned for telling the truth—the following situation could result.

Within minutes, almost the entire continent of North America and a good part of Western Europe would be ablaze. Only those regions covered by clouds would be saved—to be consumed later by the vast, moving, uncontrollable fire. There would be no fire-storms in the conventional sense because the high winds caused by blast effects do not occur in airless space. But the intense thermal radiation would penetrate through the atmosphere as if the sun itself had abruptly drawn the Earth to within a few hundred miles of its corona. The normal winds and turbulent expanding air currents would do the rest. Not much plant or animal life, including the human, would escape incineration.

Of course there might be some retaliation. SAC bombers are always in the air, flying practice missions. Chances are, however, that the major command posts, airborne as well as underground, would be knocked out by the holocaust of thermal radiation. These are designed to survive a nuclear airburst within the atmosphere or a groundburst, emanating from much smaller nuclear weapons. Against the incandescent heat from fusion devices exploded in a low orbit, 100 to 150 miles up, they might be helpless. The heat could ignite or melt almost every material—steel, copper, aluminum, wood, glass and human flesh—by conduction, absorption or convection. Much of the heat would be reflected from bright objects to darker ones, where absorption would cause ignition. It would be almost impossible to escape the holocaust. Although the molecules of air in the atmosphere would absorb a large portion of the heat, they would also scatter it in many directions at once. Enough intensity of heat would reach combustible materials on the ground to paralyze, if not thoroughly destroy, a continent by fire—without the enemy having had to dilute the element of surprise inherent in a spontaneous detonation of a half-dozen big satellites in orbit. By not sending his supermegaton devices directly to a chosen target, he can avoid detection of them en route.

Admittedly, such an attack as just described borders on fantasy, but its description is generally based on fact. Liberties have been taken with certain scientific data in order to drive home a serious realization: we are secure today because of our superior military strength, but tomorrow we may be defenseless. We have no active defense against enemy long-range ballistic missiles, although we can detect them in time to alert SAC—and this is the great discouraging factor to an enemy. He cannot surprise us, therefore he cannot paralyze us. The price he would have to pay for an attempted surprise attack would allow him no profit. On the other hand, "innocent" satellites could cross North America for a number of days, or weeks, or months before he decides that they are in the proper positions and the weather is right to detonate them by a coded radio signal from his tracking ships that have been posing as fishing trawlers off the North American coasts or from submarines that have surfaced for "harmless" maneuvers. He could even confound our intelligence sources by calling a quiescent period to military maneuvers within his own frontiers. If he is sure enough of the effectiveness of his surprise blow, he would not have to defend his homeland against retaliation anyway. He would not be deterred from starting a global war, since he would feel assured of instantaneous victory.

Naturally his judgment may be wrong. But if he *thinks* it is right, many nations and many peoples, including his own, might suffer immeasurably. The Free World must *always* keep him thinking that such a judgment *will* be wrong.

The Deputy Defense Secretary, Roswell Gilpatrick, put the situation in a nutshell when he spoke at an Aerospace Symposium held by the Air Force Academy during the late summer of 1962. "So long as we have so little knowledge of what the Soviets are doing," he said, "we must base our preparations to a significant extent on what we think they are capable of doing. This is an important consideration in view of the relatively long lead times required for the development and production of weapon systems. We cannot wait until Soviet weapons have been developed, produced and deployed in such quantities as to be evident before we begin our own cycle of development and production. Thus the Soviets are forced to work hard to match the efforts that they *know* we are making to match the efforts that we *think* they are making." (The emphasis is by Mr. Gilpatrick.)

MILITARY STRENGTH
THROUGH COUNTERMEASURES

A timeworn, and thus historically proved, axiom of weaponry development is: Equally important with the achievement of revolutionary new weapons is the development of new methods to render them useless. Military force is effective in maintaining a Government's ideals, goals and policies only insofar as that force is invincible. At least half of its effectiveness depends upon an enemy's feeling that he cannot nullify it, that it will inevitably grind him down to retreat. Thus reliable countermeasures become an integral part of military strength. If democracy is to survive, we must not only develop a striking force of inexorable power, but we must simultaneously develop countermeasures that will make an enemy see that his most devastating weapons are useless—long before we are goaded into striking him with a paralyzing blow.

General Bernard Schriever, shortly before he acquired the top rank of a fourth star, made the situation brightly clear with an apparently simple statement. "Today the kind and quality of systems which a nation develops can decide the battle in advance and make the final conflict a mere formality—or can bypass conflict altogether." He was writing in the *Air University Quarterly Review* on the theme of "The Operational Urgency of Research and Development." He added: "There can be little doubt that we are now engaged in a technological war. The opponents in this war represent the two most highly developed plans for the organization of human society—one by total absorption into the state, the other by free association between groups and persons. The side that first achieves unquestioned superiority in technical capability as well as numerical strength may well prevail over the other without any overt test in battle."

That the "Cold War," an invention of the Kremlin, is in its military aspect a technological war was sharply evidenced by the concentrated incursions of "Sputnik Diplomacy" performed by the Kremlin immediately after the Soviet Union successfully launched the world's first two man-made satellites.

On this theme, General Schriever continues: "Any important advance achieved by one side or the other is likely to have a strategic impact far beyond the tactical advantage which it confers for the time-being. Hence in modern war we find a new element raised to a level of highly organized effort for the first time: the element of technological surprise. It is the effect secured by putting into use, before the adversary does, a significant technical achievement that makes him temporarily more vulnerable."

More informally, Schriever once told me: "If the Soviets really should come up with a significant breakthrough in the field of space technology, they might be able to refuse other nations an access to space itself—even for pure scientific research. This would be the gravest kind of threat to our national security."

The word "access" has more than a casual dictionary meaning when it pertains to a military posture. Control of access usually determines the differential between victory and defeat in a specific battle as well as in a general war. Access to Cuba, for instance, was effectively controlled for twenty-eight days during October-November 1962. That quarantine of a large island "republic" was effective only because the United States Navy was capable of controlling sea access. It caused the physical defeat of certain Communist aims in the Western Hemisphere and a moral defeat for the Kremlin. Control of a bridge, a mountain pass or a junction of highways or railroads has in the past paralyzed an enemy's military operations. During the Korean War it was the ultimate superiority of USAF aircraft and pilots that barred air access to the Communists and led them to declare a cease-fire.

Probably the most important form of access in the military

sense is access to information. For if an enemy is to assure himself of supreme success in a surprise attack, his intelligence access must greatly overbalance that of the people he intends to attack. Access to information directly involves three other forms of access—reconnaissance, defense and offense. The first of these supplements and/or verifies the others. If you know where an enemy's ground-to-air missiles are located before you attack him by air, you can either avoid them, confuse them or destroy them. In the latter case, reconnaissance would verify their destruction as well as the destruction of strategic targets. The vital need for access of information in defense should be self-evident. Unless you know in advance that an enemy is attacking, you are stalemated by surprise and cannot defend yourself against him. Fortunately, at present, we control access to the seas and air of North America. We even have an intelligence access superior to the enemy's. We do not, however, control the access to space. This is unfortunate today and, if it persists—tomorrow may be tragic.

DEMOCRATIC IDEALISTS
RESIST MILITARY SPACE MISSIONS

We are accomplishing many more remarkable experiments in outer space than are the Soviets. Most of these have already revolutionized scientific thinking and theory. But for the reason, perhaps, that we are democratic idealists there has been a somewhat general resistance to the pursuit of military missions in space. The civilian NASA is justifiably proud of its tremendous progress in pure space-science researches. They feel that by freely supplying their newly discovered data to scientists of all nations, they are helping the causes of international understanding and goodwill. In the broadest way, they are right. Science by its nature must be international. If all governments pursued the same pure goals as scientists, there would be no requirement for the military superiority of one nation over another. Since that requirement, however, is real, it would be folly to ignore it. Dedi-

cated enemies of our way of life, the Communists certainly do
not ignore it.

Not long after the first sputniks were launched, a recognized
spokesman for the Red military made this obvious. Major General G. Pokrovskii published a statement: "The development of
technology . . . has led to artificial earth satellites which, together with their scientific value, also have military significance.
From them, it is possible to observe the opponent's territory
and to throw atomic bombs on that territory."

To the thoughtful person, there can be no clear demarcation
between the civilian and military purposes of space research.
Science gathers and defines new knowledge to improve the
world. The democratic military, at least, needs this same knowledge to assure that freedom may exist in the world, now and in
the future, so that scientists may continue in peace to explore
unknown frontiers of knowledge. So long as national, ideological and human boundaries exist, there will remain an American
requirement for superior military strength to keep the peace.
The much over-rated philosophy that presumes man will humbly change for the better when he sees the awesome magnificence of the Universe spread before him has not impressed the
Russians. One commentator writing in *Komsomolskaya Pravda*
(Young Communist Truth) used the sputniks as proof that
God does not exist. "We have been out in space for hundreds of
miles," he wrote in effect, "and we could find no trace of God.
Ergo, he is a myth of the Capitalists to oppress the working
class."

How can you reason with those who hold such "logic"?

General Schriever doesn't try. He strikes at the core of the
matter. "The Soviets have chosen to make a major challenge in
the area of science and military technology. They take a militant
pride in their successes in space. They present their successes to
the world as proof that Communism is the powerful wave of
the future and that Communist rule of the entire world is inevitable."

On this basis, any letup to a vigorous program aimed at both military and civilian space superiority could be fatal. Each complements the other. Each produces peaceful by-products that benefit mankind in terms of new medical discoveries, new materials, weather forecasting, communications, new manufacturing techniques and better consumer goods, as far removed from space experiments as refrigerators and television sets. Each stimulates American industry, science and technology to produce imaginative new achievements. Each helps to assure the continuing security of the Free World.

As it was once stated by the Honorable Eugene M. Zuckert, Secretary of the Air Force, "The United States Air Force, in being today, is the world's most powerful and versatile. This fact is a tribute in good part to the industrial genius and capability of America. But the accomplishment up to now is only a portent of the aerospace challenge of the future."

That challenge is already being met with the development of TITAN III. This TITAN is not a missile. It is a launch vehicle based on rigid military requirements. In civilian space research the element of time is not vitally important to a launching. Spaceflights, manned or unmanned, can be scheduled months in advance and even then be delayed because of adverse weather or mechanical conditions. A purely scientific experiment can always wait—a week, a month, a year, even a century, as physical events may demand. But a military launch vehicle, as well as a missile, must be ready to go at a moment's alarm. In the face of an immediate threat, there is no time for rescheduling. The nonsurvival of our very way of life might result from a delay.

Until the airplane became routinely reliable, it had neither military nor commercial significance. TITAN III was conceived by the Air Force and Martin-Denver engineers as a routinely reliable workhorse of the Space Age. Its feasibility grew out of the ultrahigh reliability inherent with TITAN II. It combines the best aspects of liquid- and solid-fuel development in rockets. Thus it owes a considerable debt for its existence to the earlier "hard-luck" VANGUARD. For the next decade, at least, it will be the keystone of America's military space deterrent. But it will also provide many advantages for pure science.

ROUTINE RELIABILITY FOR SPACE

TITAN III is designed as an overall military/scientific space vehicle, a heavyweight space truck to deliver payloads in much the same manner as a tractor-trailer routinely carries heavy cargo across the nation's highways. It can deliver multiton cargo, manned or unmanned, into Earth orbit or to the moon and beyond.

In one configuration, TITAN III stands 120 feet high and is 30 feet wide. This is the "C" Model, essentially a 4-stage system generating more than 2½ million pounds of thrust—or about three times the power generally estimated for the most powerful Soviet launch vehicle. The core of TITAN III is a modified version of the TITAN II ICBM. It can be used alone, stripped of the two powerful solid-fuel rockets the first stage comprises. This is the "A" Configuration.

But the most vitally important aspect of TITAN III is that it is a *complete* system. In the Free World, and so far as we know, in the whole world, it is the *first* complete space-launch system. The configurations of the launch vehicle are but half of the system. The other half is the Integrate-Transfer-Launch (ITL) Complex, with its unique mobile launchers and mobile aerospace ground support equipment. The launch vehicles provide the system with great versatility and flexibility in accomplishing space missions, while the ITL contributes the capability for almost instantaneous reaction time and a vastly increased launch rate. The ITL concept, for the first time, provides a fully controlled factory-like environment that quickly makes possible the assembly of a launch vehicle in a chosen configuration, the selection and attachment of any one of a variety of payloads, the complete checkout of all subsystems and the movement of the total assembly to a launch complex, where the vehicle is erected on its pad, counted down and held against either a planned or unplanned launch requirement. It can be held in such readiness indefinitely, with no deterioration of its capabilities.

An example of the swiftness with which this standardized system can operate is TITAN III-C: it can be transformed from a TITAN III-A in a matter of a half-dozen hours by merely detouring it through the Solid Motor Assembly Building. Two million pounds of thrust are thus added to TITAN III in those 6 hours. The advantages of such flexibility should be obvious. If an unknown spacecraft is detected far out in the void—too far out to be intercepted by TITAN III-A with a sufficiently heavy payload—the "A" Model TITAN III can be adapted to meet the situation before that spacecraft can approach close enough to demonstrate hostile intentions. Equally, upon determination of the launch of an Earth-orbital satellite by a potential enemy, the ITL can modify TITAN III to meet the possible threat of that satellite even as it establishes itself in an orbit.

Mainly, however, TITAN III stands ready on the pad at all times. If greater power or additional launch vehicles are required, the ITL can fill the gap with precision, reliability and speed.

The "A" Configuration of TITAN III consists of two redesigned TITAN II stages, a liquid-propellant transtage and a control module for the transtage. The transtage is almost a miracle of ingenuity devised by scientists and engineers of the Aerospace Corporation, the Air Force Space Systems Division, the Aerojet-General Corporation and the Denver Division of Martin Marietta Corporation. No one of these contributors to the transtage concept can be credited more than any other. Fabrication of the transtage, including the control module, is the responsibility of Martin-Denver. Technical direction for development of the transtage is the responsibility of Aerospace Corporation, in accordance with the requirements established by the Space Systems Division of the Air Force Systems Command. Aerojet-General is responsible for the transtage liquid propulsion system.

Lloyd Kohrs, Manager of the Space Propulsion Division at

Aerojet-General, calls the transtage of TITAN III "a switch engine for space."

Here's how he describes its capabilities: "It is a switch engine that turns Cape Canaveral into a universal launch site, capable of placing payloads into many orbits. With transtage, for example, a payload can be launched into equatorial orbit from Cape Canaveral just as if it had been launched from the Equator. It is designed specifically to take a payload from one orbit to another, to take a payload out of orbit and send it on an Earth-escape trajectory toward the moon or another planet, and to change a payload's inclination to the Earth. It can achieve its many missions because it can be started and stopped many times in space."

This last is a hint of the technological distance covered by the Air Force-Martin Marietta-Aerojet-General team since the days when they were worried about whether or not they could ignite the second-stage engine of TITAN I in space.

But the real significance of such versatility in a launch vehicle is that it provides the United States with a capability to intercept, inspect and destroy, if necessary, enemy satellites as soon as they are detected in the sky—regardless of the plane or distance of their orbit. Into relatively low orbits it will be able to place inspection and destruction equipment weighing 5,000 to 25,000 pounds. And as described earlier, the not-too-distant future could bring a horrifying type of nuclear surprise attack in the lower orbits.

MANNED SPACE COMMAND POSTS

The lower orbits are also important for relatively small military manned space stations in the 10- to 20-ton range. TITAN III should be able to place such a station in orbit either on a one-shot basis or by launching several sections subsequently to be connected in space. Vehicles to service these stations could easily be produced by modification of Project Gemini capsules, carrying a two-man replacement crew and cargo from the Earth. Not long ago the foregoing concepts were strictly reserved for authors of science fiction. Today, Secretary of the Air Force Zuckert can say: "A very important long-range space objective is the development of positive command and control systems sufficiently secure to insure a high degree of survival as well as the ability to communicate at will with our forces wherever they may be. Well-dispersed space stations offer very attractive possibilities for this mission."

Such orbital command posts would vastly amplify the deterrent power of SAC. It would also proportionately diminish the possibility of war by accident, since control would be triply maintained from posts underground, airborne and in space. Actually, a satellite-borne command post was proposed by SAC as a requirement in 1958 and was designated "Project Steer." Lamentably, it was dropped in 1960 by the Department of Defense, in favor of a synchronous communications satellite system called Project Advent—which has since been redirected from Army to Air Force responsibility for development, production and launch. Ground-communication development remains with the Army. Project Advent is extremely important—but so was Project Steer. Both could be realized with TITAN III.

A synchronous satellite is one that is synchronized with the Earth's rotation. Such synchronization can be obtained if a satellite is placed above the Equator at a distance of six Earth radii, or about 22,300 miles. At that position it would remain fixed in the sky and could continuously survey a large area of the world. Three satellites spaced 120° apart in that same orbit could keep every spot on Earth under surveillance and communicate among themselves as well as between all areas of the world and themselves. To the average person, the synchronous orbit may appear to be quite a distance out in space, but not to General Schriever. "I even consider the 24-hour orbit of a synchronous satellite to be a low Earth orbit," he told a reporter at an Air Force Association Space Symposium.

By implication, the visionary young General is already considering the need for military space operations beyond the outer

Van Allen Radiation Belt, a distance at least twice as far as that of the synchronous orbit. Yet only with such thinking can we out-anticipate the enemy and maintain control of the space access.

Our goals in space were concisely expressed by Lieutenant General James Ferguson in the spring of 1962 when he was testifying before the House Committee on Armed Services. He said: "The United States National Space Policy recognizes four reasons for conducting projects in space: to increase scientific knowledge, to exploit commercial applications, to strengthen military capabilities, and to enhance national prestige.

"The prime objective of the Air Force Space Policy is to exploit space so as to retain United States military superiority in order to insure the peaceful use of space." General Ferguson is USAF's Deputy Chief of Staff for Research and Technology, a man who intimately knows the importance of staying far ahead in the technological cold war.

In terms of time, the maintenance of such a lead can be compared to a skyscraper. Most of the planning and energy that went into its imposing appearance is hidden from sight in structural steel. The time involved in its construction was a minor part of the total effort to conceive of its multifarious components and design these into a functional entity. This is what military planners mean by the phrase "lead time."

The lead time required by military systems is, of course, much more intricate and extended than the basic architectural planning for a skyscraper. Fundamentally, it depends upon an awareness of a potential enemy's capabilities and intent—and then out-performing the best of which he is capable. In military space this becomes exceedingly complex. The systems must perform routinely in an environment thoroughly alien, as well as hostile, to man and his machines. The assurance of routine reliability demands excessive testing in that environment, first to prove the feasibility of the system and then to sharpen its reliability. This costs money, and budget-conscious administrators, military as well as civilian, often try to knock down a system needed for the future before its feasibility can be proved in the present. Yet without that proof the system will not be ready if or when it is urgently needed. For reasons of survival alone, any logically proposed system should be given the chance to prove its feasibility.

"If you run out of dollar bills, you can print new ones. But if you run out of time, you can't buy it back," was the way that lead-time requirements were expressed to me by Lieutenant Colonel William H. Moore in the Requirements and Standardization Office of Program 624A.

That is the program to develop the Air Force's SSLV, or Standardized Space-Launch Vehicle, popularly called TITAN III. I had visited Colonel Moore and others in his office at the new Aerospace Corporation Complex in order to discuss the future of TITAN III. At the time, it was in the feasibility proposal stage and a test program had not yet been approved officially.

AURA OF THE FUTURE

The then brand new Aerospace Corporation, a nonprofit scientific and engineering organization to advise the Air Force as did the Space Technology Laboratories before it, had about it an aura of the future. It was as far removed in knowledge and appearance from the old parochial school of the Western Development Division as STL had been removed from WDD. It was in El Segundo, separated from the Inglewood Complex by the now-expanded Los Angeles International Airport. Many times larger, the new complex suggested the Space Age with its rows of tall buildings, all cleanly designed in a display of glass, marble and concrete. Sunken Japanese gardens with sculptured fountains emphasized the exotic mood. But sternly underneath that mood was the deadly seriousness of security. You couldn't get by the guarded receptionist in any of the buildings without the proper clearance or escort for that particular building.

I asked Colonel Moore about the future of TITAN III. He was enthusiastic and assuring. There was no question in his mind that it would be approved for development in time. "We are hoping," he said, "that in the development program we can consider not only the capabilities of this launch vehicle but also all of the possible proposed uses for it. We hope that we can influence the direction of those uses, the various space missions, into a realistic pattern to insure that TITAN III does have a logical growth potential. In this way we can take care of those uses that might be required later. What I'm really trying to say is: We hope that TITAN III will be the balancing force between a variety of space-missions, some of which may not yet be evident. In other words, TITAN III will be available as standard hardware. It would have all the desirable attributes of economy, simplicity and reliability. Before this, every new space mission required new developments to test it. In fact, rocket modifications were often required for every twist of the test mission after it got started. But the realistic thing about TITAN III is that almost any space mission can be tailored to suit it."

Major Jon Launderville, who was also present, elaborated. "The original ICBM just wasn't designed for a space job. It's a weapon system built to knock out targets. But today we're using modified ballistic missiles such as THOR and the ATLAS —and later on, we'll be using a version of TITAN II—and when a mission comes along that requires their thrust, in most cases you have to modify them. If you place a high requirement of reliability on the mission—higher than that required for the missile itself—then you have to pay a terrific price in the development of what amounts to a new system. Each space booster then becomes almost a separate development of its own. Whereas, if you optimize the launch vehicle, as the TITAN III would be optimized, it could be used for a wide range of missions. These could be fitted into a part of the configuration spectrum of TITAN III and could thus be handled without any large change in the configuration of a missile. So TITAN III would be a lower-cost item, because it would be developed as a standard off-the-shelf item."

How had the TITAN III concept come into being? I asked Launderville. He answered that he believed "The Martin Company and the Air Force Space Systems Division both reviewed the feasibility of modifying TITAN II so that big solid-propellant rockets could be 'strapped on' its sides. I think that was how the idea was born. And when this concept was thoroughly examined in Washington by the Golovin Committee to investigate large launch vehicles and by several other people of importance, they agreed that this concept was a possible workhorse for many proposed payloads. They felt that it had a greater payload-range potential than anything we've ever had before."

Actually, however, the TITAN III concept grew from the Phoenix Study, a military scientific and engineering study conducted by the Air Force to investigate its entire spectrum of space-launch requirements for the immediate and more distant future. The concept was then presented to the Golovin Committee (the popular designation for the Large Launch Vehicle Group), established as a joint civilian and military committee of experts by James Webb, Administrator of NASA, and Robert McNamara, Secretary of Defense. This group studies all proposals for the development of big space-launch vehicles in terms of two strictly different requirements—those demanded by military operations and those needed for the purely scientific exploration of space. The group felt that the SATURN family of launch vehicles could satisfy NASA's scientific research requirements. TITAN III development by the Air Force was recommended to satisfy the military requirements.

The first of a long series of such requirements to be satisfied was Project X-20. A modified TITAN II ICBM was discontinued as its space booster and supplanted by the TITAN III Standard Launch Vehicle. Originally known as DYNA-SOAR (for "Dynamic Soaring"), Project X-20 had dawdled on the drawing boards for many years before TITAN II came along. Essentially it is a manned satellite with wings designed to permit the pilot-astronaut to descend from orbit and land on a runway of his choice, like a conventional airplane. Its tactical advantages are obvious. As a research vehicle, it could prove the feasibility of manned orbital reconnaissance.

The X-20 could investigate and produce important engineering data on stability, control and re-entry through the atmosphere to aid in the development of a variety of routinely reliable manned spacecraft. This last is its major purpose. Simply, it is known as an MTS, a Military Test System. The problems involved with flight-testing it are not so simple.

WELL WORTH THE EFFORT

However, the difficulties are well worth the effort required to conquer them. For future X-20-related spacecraft might be developed that could perform rescue missions in space and bring back the rescued to hospitals. Or these spacecraft could rendezvous with and dock on space stations to transfer information (such as reconnaissance photos) and supplies. They might even be developed for strategic bombing missions, from which they could return to a SAC base on Earth for new supplies and weapons. Their very presence could be the mightiest of deterrents to an enemy bent on world conquest.

Originally, the DYNA-SOAR plan was to take its test program in easy steps. First, there were to have been a series of suborbital flights down the Atlantic Missile Range, with landings on successively more distant islands. For this purpose, TITAN I was chosen as the launch vehicle. But mighty as that ICBM is, it could not cope with the ever-increasing weight that was being designed into the DYNA-SOAR glider by Boeing, the principal contractor. The weight was necessary, since the ultimate stresses that the vehicle would have to endure were almost wholly unknown. As it was put to me by Jack Trenholm, Deputy Director of the Project in the DYNA-SOAR Systems Office at the Wright Aeronautical Systems Division near Dayton, Ohio: "You've got the pilot's life to think about. So you overdesign everything, make it stronger than you even think it has to be, add every extra system that you can to keep the safety factor real high."

Because of this factor, the scheduling on the X-20 DYNA-SOAR had to be continually advanced—until nobody was actually certain when it would be launched. Today, a firm schedule has been established for late 1964, thanks to the introduction of the TITAN III Program, which is also now well underway with official approval and contracts awarded to the Martin Marietta Corporation as integrating contractor, to Aerojet-General for the storable liquid-fuel engines and to United Aircraft Corporation for the big solid-fuel first-stage booster-rockets. Six astronauts are already in training to pilot the DYNA-SOAR glider in orbit and back to Earth by "dead-stick." The first manned test flight will be orbital. Launch will be from Cape Canaveral, Florida, with a descent from orbit for a landing at Edwards Air Force Base in the Mojave Desert of California.

At Edwards AFB for several years now, quietly lost in the blare of more spectacular space missions, the X-15 Program has been moving ahead with unusually high success. Three of these experimental rocket-powered aircraft are continually in use to explore areas of hypersonic flight at extreme altitudes. The X-15 is in every sense a forerunner of DYNA-SOAR. It has gathered engineering data without which the X-20 could not even be designed. One X-15 test-pilot, Major Bob White, has earned his Astronaut Wings by flying the craft above 50 miles altitude.

The X-15 operates on an almost routine schedule and has developed extremely reliable stability and control systems that will be vital to routine manned space missions. This black missile-shaped research airplane is dropped from under the wing of a B-52 mother ship at an altitude of about 8 miles over Wendover Air Force Base in Nevada. It then ignites its rocket engine and climbs toward the fringe of the atmosphere to perform numerous experiments before it glides without power to a landing on one of the dry lake beds surrounding Edwards Air Force Base.

Both the X-15 and X-20 as were all the pure X-type aircraft
before them, represent a collaborative effort between the military and the civilian organization now known as NASA. This is
as it should be in a democracy. Nor is there any duplication of
effort between TITAN III, an Air Force Program, and NASA's
giant SATURN and NOVA launch boosters. The latter are
required to be extremely reliable so that manned flights may be
made to the moon and planets for scientific research, but they
are not required to have the capability of standing by in readiness for instant missions, a vital necessity if we are to have a
superior space deterrent.

Each learns from the other. TITAN III will undoubtedly
carry out many NASA missions as well, after a sufficient number of vehicles are available. What NASA discovers in its Project
Gemini rendezvous and docking experiments will also benefit
the Air Force just as the Air Force has benefited Gemini in advance with certain information. "The rendezvous studies made
in our program have contributed significantly to the NASA rendezvous program," I was told by Colonel Eugene A. Blue, Director of Air Force Program 621A.

The 621A Program is working on the development of a prototype satellite with the capability of inspecting and reporting
on other satellites in orbit. Unlike the X-20 DYNA-SOAR, it is
an unmanned vehicle. Although it was planned initially to be
launched on test flights sometime within the next year or so by
an ATLAS-AGENA-B combination, its ultimate operational
launch vehicle will be TITAN III, or Program 624A, which was
approved much later by the Department of Defense. Recently,
the 621A Program was reoriented toward achieving longer term
space applications than were originally projected. These are
security-classified. Actually, only the program number identifies
these projects to the Air Staff in the Pentagon, but almost all
projects have popular names. Program 621A, before its reorien-
tation, was called the "Satellite-Inspector." It has been known
by a variety of names since it was first initiated some 5 years before 624A.

SAINTS OF ALL COLORS

When the program was started in 1958 (an indication of Air Force farsightedness), it was called SAINT, for "Satellite Inspection Techniques." It was a feasibility study that covered several possible approaches. To prevent confusion among them, each was given a different color designation. The GREEN SAINT was a ground-launched vehicle for live demonstrations to prove that satellite inspection was possible. The contract for this part of the program was awarded to RCA, which is now actively engaged in building the hardware. A SILVER SAINT was to be a test satellite launched from a jet bomber at high altitudes. The ultimate operational unmanned inspector satellite was dubbed WHITE SAINT, and BLUE SAINT was to be a manned inspection system for the distant future. The BLUE SAINT approach has since been turned over to the X-20 DYNA-SOAR Program, which has gained, and will continue to gain, a considerable amount of valuable data from studies made on the unmanned portion of 621A.

SAINT as a name did not last long. Many religious groups that felt that it was highly improper for a military weapon system to have such a holy connotation put pressure on the Defense Department. The Secretary of the Air Force finally had to issue a directive that the name be changed. It was changed to HAWKEYE, until everybody discovered that the Navy had previously given that name to one of its airplanes. So the Air Force went back to SAINT. Again there was heavy protest. At this point, the Secretary decided that numbers were more precise than names anyway. Thus our hope for the future to prevent a surprise nuclear attack from space is wrapped up in a serial-number, 621A.

By a very happy, if disconcerting, coincidence, the 621A Program people had no trouble at all in selling the Pentagon on funding a live feasibility demonstration of the unmanned inspector satellite. "Lonesome George," an unidentified satellite, was picked up orbiting across the skies of North America by the tracking network of NORAD's Space Detection and Tracking Center. For awhile, it was assumed in Washington that the unknown satellite, which was transmitting no radio signals, was Russian. Moscow denied this vigorously. But, of course, you can't trust Moscow. This time, however, they were telling the truth. Lonesome George was at last identified as one of the initial Air Force DISCOVERER Satellites that had not burned up in the atmosphere, as everybody had previously assumed. The incident occurred during the early days before NORAD's space-detection system was "tuned up" to the level of its present perfection.

But how can you tell whether a satellite, unknown or admittedly Russian, is carrying nuclear devices for hostile purposes? The obvious ways are by using television cameras and sensing devices at close range to note the size, measure the radiations emanating from it, nuclear and electromagnetic, and measure its mass or weight.

"Wouldn't it be a little tricky to determine the mass of a satellite in orbit?" I asked Colonel Blue.

"Well, we've got a number of techniques that we are considering," he answered. "But if I told you what they were, I'd be giving away classified information."

Destruction of a hostile enemy satellite was not included as part of the original feasibility demonstration program. "However," as Colonel Blue says, "an operational satellite inspector might have this capability." The suggestion is that some other program could be working on this phase for the future. It could even be a part of the reoriented 621A Program. Meanwhile, if we develop the ability to inspect and analyze the character of satellites in orbit, that in itself will provide a strong deterrent to an enemy surprise nuclear attack. For SAC bombers and missile squadrons will be warned in time to retaliate. We have no such inspection capability at the moment, but it is to be hoped that the lead time required by us to develop one will be less than the Kremlin lead time requirement for placing nuclear weapons in orbit.

For the immediate future, other satellite weapon systems are urgently needed to extend our lead in military space. Programs to study and develop these are vigorously being pursued. They are a Missile Detection and Alarm System (MIDAS), a Ballistic Missile Bombardment Intercept System (BAMBI) and an unmanned reconnaissance satellite that cannot be identified for security reasons. The MIDAS Program has recently been reoriented to develop a simpler, more reliable system than earlier test-flown models. Although no funds have yet been appropriated for an operational MIDAS, the research and development program is adequately funded. Its aim is to produce satellites that can detect the launch of enemy long-range ballistic missiles as they rise above the pad and thus provide NORAD with a 30-minute advance warning—twice the warning time provided by the present Ballistic Missile Early Warning System (BMEWS). BAMBI is in the feasibility study stage only at present. On paper, it is a satellite weapon that would not merely detect the launching of enemy ICBMs but would immediately destroy such missiles as well. The importance of reconnaissance satellites needs no elaboration.

RELAY STATIONS IN RANDOM ORBITS

One of the most interesting proposals for a satellite system that would help to guarantee our military control of access to the space environment was proposed by Donald L. Haas, Manager of Advanced Programs/Communications at Martin Marietta's Orlando, Florida subdivision. The system would be based on the revolutionary RACEP communications approach, earlier described in Chapter Three. Mr. Haas read a technical paper on his proposal, which has not been officially authorized by the Government, at an annual meeting of the Air Force Association in the fall of 1962. He proposed a network of nuclear-powered satellites, each carrying a RACEP unit. With 57 satellites, weighing only about 250 pounds apiece with all their required equipment, a vast communications and control network can be maintained indefinitely among a million users on the ground, in the air, or at sea. The satellites would not have to be in precision orbits, making their launching task simpler, since RACEP is not bothered by radio interference from other transmitters on the same channel due to its technique of coding pulsed signals. The RACEP satellites could be shot into random orbits a thousand miles out and would act as relay stations to cover the world. These are not ordinary relay stations. Because of the portability of RACEP, they could relay messages in voice or code between jeeps, supply carriers such as ships and trucks, submarines, airplanes and missile squadrons or batteries. Each of the relay satellites would have a dozen one-way channels and six simultaneous full duplex transmissions in any combination of voice or data. The advantage of such a system to the survivability of SAC Command Posts and NORAD or Army, Navy and Air Force combat operations, for that matter, would be tremendous. Every combat vehicle, from an ICBM stored underground to a counter-insurgency helicopter hovering over the jungles, would be within easy communications range of the RACEP satellites. In fact, a counter-guerrilla group cutting its way through those same jungles could communicate not only with the helicopter and their headquarters but also with staff headquarters in the Pentagon. Simultaneously, on a global basis, all combat forces and intelligence-gathering organizations could be in touch with each other, on a reliable minute-by-minute daily basis if this were required. The Command Over-ride feature of RACEP would also give the President of the United States or the Joint Chiefs of Staff the instant ability to talk with all commanders in the field, world-wide. The value of this kind of communications network to the United States STRIKE Command alone is immeasurable.

The proposed satellite communications network is made even more attractive from a military viewpoint because of the long life and dependability of nuclear power plants in the satellites. The first of the Navy's navigational satellites, TRANSIT IV-A, to have its electrical power supplied by a nuclear source was launched on June 28, 1961. It is still transmitting loud and clear.

That power plant was of grapefruit-size and small wattage. Produced by the Martin-Nuclear Division in Baltimore, it is a mere forerunner of satellite nuclear power to come. Approximately a year later, Martin-Nuclear was awarded a feasibility study contract by the Atomic Energy Commission to design and develop a 500-watt nuclear generator that could be used in much bigger satellites.

Martin-Orlando, as well as Hughes Aircraft, IBM, Bell Telephone Laboratories, General Electric, and many other leading members of the aerospace industry, are hard at work in an especially interesting new area of research and development that may ultimately transform the very nature of spaceborne deterrent power. It should also provide almost numberless civilian applications, many of them as yet unguessed, to the great advantage of the average citizen.

This exciting new field of engineering and physical research is that of the LASER, an acronym for "Light Amplification by Stimulated Emission of Radiation." Simply, a LASER is an optical system that organizes light rays of a single wave length —for example, deep red—into parcels of concentrated energy, which may then be focused with high accuracy upon a close or distant target. The energy of light, because of its considerably shorter wave lengths, is much greater than that of heat or radio. But light exists normally in such a diffuse fashion, moving randomly in all directions at once, that its intense energy is hardly noticed. A thin piece of paper or metallic foil can stop it. Ordinary lenses and mirrors merely focus rays to points on a plane and thus apparently bring order out of the normal chaos. A LASER, on the other hand, forces *all* of the energy into a single plane and direction before it is focused. LASER beams have already been used to drill holes in steel and to bounce signals off the moon. Brain surgery is one future civilian application for these beams.

The possibilities inherent in LASERs for military space operations are stunning. General Ferguson only touched on the possibilities when he testified before a subcommittee of the House

Committee on Appropriations for the 1963 fiscal Air Force budget. Yet what he said gives a strong hint of the variety of those possibilities. "Reaching further into our future technology," he began, "I can report on two of the most significant recent developments in the entire field of electronics. One of these, known as LASER . . . is the first device capable of generating or amplifying pure . . . single-frequency light. . . . This development allows us to use light in the same manner that we use radio today. A single LASER is capable of accommodating 5,000 normal TV channels. A 10-kilowatt LASER with a 10-foot (diameter) reflector (for focusing) will be capable of communicating with the entire solar system. Long-range surveillance of space vehicles using an optical radar (known as 'ladar') is within reach." The second recent development referred to by General Ferguson is an electric rocket engine for deep space operations.

DEATH RAY FROM A LIGHT BEAM

General Schriever himself, as he delivered the keynote address at the Seventh Annual Technical Symposium of the Society of Photographic Instrumentation Engineers, had this to say:

"The LASER is ideally suited for application in space. One of its uses will be as part of various sensing devices. . . . Data readout, mapping, surveying and navigation and control may be revolutionized by the full application of the LASER principle.

"The LASER offers a method for communications and energy transfer in space. If a high-energy LASER beam were directed at a satellite, most of its energy could be transferred to an appropriate receiver. Thus it would be entirely possible to recharge batteries or activate a chemical power source in a space vehicle. If a LASER system were developed as a backup to the space vehicle's normal power supply, it could correct for a power failure.

"This same capability could also be used for defensive purposes in space. With an increase in the energy level of a LASER beam, or with more precise aiming techniques, it might have increasingly destructive and lethal effects and perhaps could be used to degrade or destroy the sensors and structure of the [enemy] space vehicle at which it was directed."

In other words, the LASER can be adapted for use as that old terror of science fiction writers—the death ray—among its many other uses. Present funding for LASER technology in the Air Force is about 6 million dollars.

The LASER resulted from a bold, broad, imaginative approach to science. Its concept was drawn from a number of scientific fields—nuclear physics, quantum optics and solid-state electronics, to list a few. Only by fusing these diverse specializations together was the concept possible. Only the most forward-looking of scientists could have accomplished this feat. Yet, as I have tried to emphasize, a majority of fine scientists are rather narrow in their viewpoint when it comes to subjects outside their immediate specializations.

Prejudice in any form not only retards progress but is anti-democratic. One of the world's foremost astrophysicists has spent a good part of his professional life trying to impress his fellow-scientists with this point. He is Dr. Fritz Zwicky of the California Institute of Technology. He calls his approach "the morphological method." The dictionary defines "morphology" as "the branch of biology dealing with the form and structure of animals and plants; the science of structural organic types." Dr. Zwicky, delivering the Halley Lecture at Oxford University, defines his use of the word as follows:

"The essence of the morphological method is direct thinking and direct action. This combination would appear to be the major asset of free men and of the democratic way of life. If this way of life is to survive, this asset must be developed and its results must be developed with all the means at our disposal.

"Morphological thinking will not be popular among dictators. It can only succeed if we let no doctrines or prejudices stand in our way. Its application will have to overcome severe obstacles even in the field of general science where objectivity and tolerance are often not as widespread as they are supposed to be. Indeed, the morphologist is not just a scientist who busies himself with problems in a specific field, thus establishing himself as a respectable astronomer, physicist, biologist and so on. The morphologist for the solution of his problems will trespass into many fields. He will thus arouse the anger of those professionals who may have great special knowledge but who fail to see beyond the boundaries of their domain."

Dr. Zwicky made the foregoing observations on May 12, 1948. They are even more valid today.

Why, for example, did it take the detection of that first thermonuclear explosion in Russia to shake some logic into the thinking of our most powerful opponents against an American ICBM program? And why, as Jack Trenholm of the DYNA-SOAR Project Office told me, was "Sputnik the biggest hotfoot the United States ever had?" He added: "No doubt about it, a lot of things started from that day. One month after Sputnik we got approval to go ahead with DYNA-SOAR." This project, I might add, had been practically "mothballed" since about 1955 by all except a small group of civilian and Air Force visionaries. It was the ICBM situation all over again.

If democracy is to live, we cannot afford to wait for further hotfoots. One of these might come so far after the fact of a new Soviet technology in weaponry that our lead time will be no time.

Paraphrasing the Communist Manifesto, we have nothing to lose but our freedom—unless we maintain the will and imagination to win.

INDEX